THE FINAL EXAM

Advanced Class
Test Guide

by
Dick Bash - KL7IHP

Bash Educational Services

P.O. Box 2115 • San Leandro, California 94577 • USA

ABOUT THE AUTHOR

Dick was born and raised in the Indianapolis, Indiana area and attended college at Indiana University and Purdue University and did his graduate work at the University of Southern California. Graduating from Purdue in January, 1972, he combined his interest in teaching and aviation by specializing in classroom instruction on jet aircraft, such as the Learjet and the Boeing 727. It was while attending Purdue that Dick obtained his Technician Class License.

After moving to Alaska in 1974, he worked as a flight engineer and also acquired his KL7IHP call sign. Still a Technician, he let his interest in Amateur Radio lapse but kept his license current in hopes he would get back on the air. After living overseas, where he flew for various airlines as a Boeing 707 and 727 flight engineer, he returned to the U.S. and renewed his interest in ham radio, determined to get his code speed up and obtain the General Class License.

After struggling with the code he received his General Class License and went on to pursue the Advanced. Suffering the same fate as 69% of the other applicants, he promptly failed the written exam. Getting together with several other hams in the San Francisco area, he studied and researched the material on the exam and finally passed it. Feeling that it was unfair to have 7 out of 10 hams fail the test, he wrote the series **THE FINAL EXAM** in hopes that other hams would have an easier time preparing for the exam. Your comments on how to help Dick make this the best manual in the country are always welcome. Send your comments to the address on the card in the back of the manual.

Dick's station consists of a Kenwood TS-180S and a Hy-Gain TH3MK3 up 32 feet and a Hy-Gain 18 HT vertical. His 2 meter radio is a Kenwood TR-2400. Feeling that we have to support 10 meters or lose it, he is around 28.600 mHz when he has some free time or on 14.280 or 14.240 mHz. Between the fun of running his company and playing with his Apple II Plus computer, he stays busy. Also he still enjoys flying and teaching aviation related subjects at Sierra Academy of Aeronautics at Oakland Airport. He worked 1,128 contacts while at Kwajalein Island and his Marshall Island callsign is KX6QK.

PREFACE

In August, 1979 a revolution slowly began as a group of hams in the San Francisco Bay area decided that the failure rate on the F.C.C. amateur radio exams was extraordinarily high (69%). In order to combat this failure rate and break the grip it was holding on the growth of ham radio, we began publishing **THE FINAL EXAM.** The material for the book was obtained by interviewing applicants for the exams and collecting the questions they had on their exams. These applicants remembered the questions and answers and we researched the material and printed the manuals. People began passing the Advanced Class written exam who had failed it four or more times in the past.

The principle reason for their failure was not that they didn't study. It was because the material they studied was not on the exams and there was no single text that contained all (or even most) of the material the F.C.C. was asking questions about. By late May, 1980 the passing rate nationwide was 55% instead of 31%. The effect of our manuals was being felt by the government, clubs, other publishers, the ham population in general, amateur radio instructors, and dealers across the country. The "established" publishers were (and still are) against our method. Only two publishers (CQ Magazine and Worldradio) would/will carry our advertisements. We have seen deceit, lies, slander, and confusion hurled at us and we were tempted to give up a multitude of times.

But daily we received the thanks of hams whose backgrounds ranged from an astronaut to bus driver to nuclear scientist to high school janitor. Our phone was busy constantly answering the many questions that came from these supporters. But for their unfailing support, we would have quit and resigned ourselves to the fact that "tradition" was king. Our budget and income were stretched to ridiculous limits. Our staff consisted of volunteers (and still does for the most part) who wanted to make some contribution for the greater good of ham radio.

That brings us to this printing and you. Behind this preface you will find the most accurate test guide in the United States. It is by hams and for hams. We're still a tiny operation and it's the little guy's way of entering the world of hams and the friendships that spring from that. We give you a personal touch that the major publishers can't give. Your predecessors have made this manual possible, as will you make the next version possible. We beg you not to copy the manual because it is the only income we have. We don't publish a magazine or manufacture things on the side. We just do one thing and we do that well: use standard military intelligence procedures to collect and disseminate the data. Our research staff is getting bigger and we're going to do some exciting things soon.

If we are ever successful, it will be because of you, the individual ham. We have vowed not to abuse the trust and friendship you have extended us and welcome any comments you might have on how we can better serve you. Beginning soon we will monitor various 2 meter and HF frequencies so you can call in and chat (no business, please). Thanks a million for your support and rest assured that we are working literally day and night to produce the finest (if not necessarily the prettiest) manuals around.

Turn the pages now and embark upon the study that will get you upgraded. Remember: **Upgrading shouldn't be degrading.** From now on it won't be!

Richard M. Bash - KL7IHP
San Leandro, California

HOW TO TAKE THE F.C.C. TEST

This examination can be very rough for someone who's not "test savvy." You may have heard that there is a trick to passing a multiple choice type examination and I agree.

Firstly, the night before the exam, get at least 7 hours of sleep and get up about 6 A.M. (that's the price of success, friend). Secondly, I want you to get a **decent** breakfast so that your blood sugar level isn't too low. Thirdly, re-read this **entire** examination guide. Finally, **write** out each of the formulas that you need to memorize about 6 times each. It'll help you remember them.

When you arrive at the testing facility, you might as well relax because you are going to pass and being relaxed about the inevitable makes good sense. You came to take a test, so let's get it over with. Look at all the DX just waiting for you!

When you are given your exam, sit down and, on the scratch paper, write out (from memory) all of the formulas IMMEDIATELY! Next, start with the first question. Read it. Attention speed readers: slow down to about 250 w.p.m. If you cannot answer the question in the same amount of time that it took you to read the question, then SKIP IT and just go on to the next question. Skip all of the questions involving calculations and/or schematics, no matter how easy they might be. When you get to the last question you have probably used up about 20 minutes or so and answered around half of the questions. Now go back to the first question you skipped and go over it again. If it's a calculation or a schematic—SKIP IT! Then go on to the next question that you skipped on your first pass through the exam. When you've made two passes through the exam, start at the front of the exam again and include all of the calculations. If you have trouble with one, SKIP IT and press on! The fourth pass will take in the schematics. By the time you've finished this pass, you probably have 25–35 questions finished. STOP!! **Stand up and stretch** and then sit back down and finish up the exam.

I like to take hard candy with me to the exam to keep my mouth wet. Seems to help a bit. Smokers, take some gum or Life-Savers. Also remember that the guy who wrote the test probably knows less about radio than you do, so **relax.**

If you've read this exam guide about **10 times** or so, the answers to the questions will tend to jump at you. **NEVER** change an answer. Invariably, you'll change it from the right answer to a wrong one.

On those new questions or ones you can't remember the answer to (probably because you didn't read through this manual **enough** times), first eliminate all of the obviously wrong answers. That'll generally leave two to choose from. One of the two choices may be a general misconception. Read carefully. Answers that contain the words "always," "must," "only," or "never" are incorrect about 75% of the time, so keep your guard up on those. Look for key words in the answer. On calculations, have a ballpark idea of what the answer **should** be. Always use a calculator and be comfortable using it too. When in doubt, after you've done all of this and still can't figure it out—GUESS! An **intelligent** guess involves all of the above. If you have a so-called "hunch," play it as a last resort. But be sure to *put some kind of answer down!*

After turning in the exam and getting your score, leave the room and write down all you can remember, for your sake, mine, and the other hams. Be sure to write down the easy questions and *also* ones that appear in this manual. That'll serve as a confidence builder for you. If you want to participate in keeping this manual up to date (and I sure hope you will!), then complete the card in the back of this manual and return it to me. If you take the guide to the exam with you, carry it in a paper sack and leave it with the person giving the exams when you take the test. Don't worry about the F.C.C. seeing your manual. I can assure you that they are only too aware of its existence.

Some of the things I've mentioned here are obvious and others are corny. TRUST ME! This system was developed for foreign students whose English was "none too good" and it works for them. It'll work for you too. Once again, **spend the time studying** the manual and believe you're going to pass, because YOU ARE! Good luck.

LEARNING TIP ...

This is a good place to discuss how to memorize a lot of numbers. In my career as a pilot and flight engineer, I have had to memorize about 11.73 zillion numbers for every bloody aircraft I flew. The way people in my capacity do it (if they want to do it the *easy* way) is to make up the old 3rd grade flashcards. Go buy yourself a packet of 3″ × 5″ index cards. Cut them in two so you have a card that's now 3″ × 2½″. On the front side of the card write a question, such as "What are the exclusive Extra Class voice frequencies?" and on the other side of the card write the answer. Also put on the cards those little areas that are hard to recall. Each individual has something that he plays heck remembering. What one person can recall easily you may have a tough time remembering. Make out a card for that son of a gun! Carry the cards around in your shirt pocket/purse with a rubber band wrapped around them. Anytime you're in an elevator, riding a bus, sitting on the "throne," eating lunch, etc. read the damn flashcards!!! The true measure of a professional is that he utilizes his time so much better than other people. Use a professional approach to the problem of learning these numbers. I know this sounds a bit nutty but it works. If it didn't, would T.W.A., United, etc. be using this method? Also, please let me know if you feel that this is something our company should get printed up for you. We do respond to customer requests if there are enough of them. Also, what should the price be? Let us hear from you!

1 At what intervals must a repeater be identified by voice or CW?

At intervals not exceeding 10 minutes.

2 If CW is used to identify a repeater, at what maximum speed may the identification be transmitted?

At not more than 20 words per minute.

3 What are A2 emissions?

This is audio frequency shift keying (AFSK) and is a form of teletype used in the VHF band and isn't permitted below 50.1 MHz.

4 The transistor equivalents of the tube's plate, grid, and cathode are what?

TUBE	_TRANSISTOR_
Plate	**Collector**
Grid	**Base**
Cathode	**Emitter**

5 Because of a possible conflict with aircraft, the F.C.C. requires that you apply through their offices when you wish to erect an antenna higher than 200 feet above the ground (WOW!) AND ALSO WHENEVER YOUR ANTENNA IS TO BE WITHIN 5000 FEET OF A RUNWAY. There are additional provisions in 97.45 but they don't concern us. If you get into big antenna towers, etc. or get near an airport (ugh!!!), you'll need to know what the term "antenna height above the average terrain" means (it's also on the test, friend). The definition is:

The height above mean sea level of the antenna's center of radiation, less the height of the average terrain.

6 The frequency shift associated with F1 RTTY emissions may not exceed what value, per F.C.C. regulations?

900 Hertz.

7 What is the highest amount of modulation permitted by F.C.C. regulations?

The maximum permissable modulation is 100%.

8 Identify an NPN and PNP transistor from a schematic symbol choice.

This is an *easy* question! Here's an "NPN" transistor:

Note that the arrow (called an emitter; same as a cath-ode in a tube) is *Not Pointing iN* (NPN), while the "PNP" is the opposite:

As you can see, the arrow on the PNP is a *Pointing iN Pointer*. Piece of cake, right?

9 Sporadic-E propagation occurs in what amateur bands?

It's somewhat common on 6 meters (50–54 MHz) and rather rare on 2 meters.

10 At what times of the day can you expect a peaking in the Sporadic-E ionization?

It is most intense in the mid-morning and early evening. However, the actual exam may ask for "late afternoon" instead of evening. Also, it's more intense in the spring and early summer. Sporadic-E ionization *may occur* during daylight *or* darkness! Avoid answers that restrict you to either daylight or dark, because it just ain't so!

11 What is the advantage of a crystal oscillator?

Better frequency stability *or* greater frequency stabilization.

12 The efficiency of an antenna system is the ratio of what to what?

It is the ratio of the driving power (from the transmitter) to the effective radiated power or ERP. The ERP is a function of the gain of the antenna and the losses within the system. The better the gain, with all other things remaining the same, the greater the efficiency of the system because you're going to get more out of the antenna for a given amount of input.

13 Define "power factor."

There are three (3) correct definitions. Know them all! Firstly, *it's the cosine of the angle between the voltage and the current.* Also, it's termed the ratio of the reactance to the resistance. Lastly, it's the ratio of real power to apparent power.

14 What are A5 or F5 emissions?

Amplitude or frequency modulated television signals.

15 An Advanced Class licensee's operating privileges include transmitting radio signals on which of the following frequencies?

14253 kHz. Boy (*Not* a chauvinistic statement!), you'd better get that frequency table memorized!

4

16 Refer to the following circuit. What does the Zener diode do?

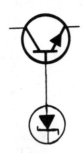

Provides a reference voltage.

17 A class AB amplifier being driven by a sine wave signal has an operating angle of what?

More than 180 degrees but less than 360 degrees. This is pure unadulterated @#★@!?%!!! Memorize the answer, pass the test, and then forget it.

18 What frequencies are affected by "Sporadic-E" clouds (transient patches of heavily ionized air)?

50 to 54 MHz is what they're looking for.

19 What may an amateur radio operator use a dip meter to determine?

The resonant frequency of antenna traps.

20 To reduce the probability of cross modulation occurring in the "front end" of an HF communications receiver, the RF amplifier stage should have what?

The RF amplifier stage should only have enough gain to allow weak signals to overcome the noise generated in the first mixer stage. On page 427 of Shrader's you'll see where he discusses this lovely subject and makes mention of the "birdies" that can be produced from a very *strong* signal.

21 Determine the phase angle in the circuit shown below:

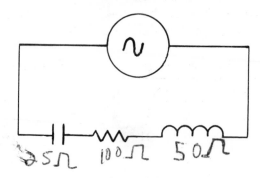

The phase angle is equal to the arctangent of the net reactance divided by the total resistance. Mathematically it looks like this:

$$P.A. = Arctan \frac{X}{R}$$

In this equation, X is equal to the inductive reactance minus the capacitive reactance $(X = X_L - X_C)$.

$$X = 50\Omega - 25\Omega$$
$$X = 25\Omega$$

The value of R is taken from the circuit and is 100Ω. We can now substitute the values for X and R in our equation like so:

$$P.A. = Arctan \frac{25}{100}$$
$$P.A. = Arctan \, 0.25$$

You would now punch 0.25 into a scientific calculator and determine the arctangent in degrees. Should you not have such a calculator (why?), then you will have to use the table of tangents given on the exam.

To use the table of trig functions (shown below) to determine the arctangent, enter the tangent column and proceed down it vertically until you find a number that is about the same as the result of dividing the net reactance by the total resistance (0.25).

Natural Trigonometric Functions

DEGREES	SIN	COS	TAN
10	0.17363	0.98481	0.17633
11	0.19091	0.98157	0.19468
12	0.20791	0.97815	0.21256
13	0.22495	0.97437	0.23087
14	0.24192	0.97030	0.24933
15	0.25882	0.96593	0.26795
16	0.27564	0.96126	0.28675
17	0.29237	0.95630	0.30573
18	0.30902	0.95106	0.32492

We see that the closest value is 0.24933. By looking straight across to the left, we can see that 0.24933 is the arctangent of 14 degrees. Therefore, the arctangent of 0.25 is about 14 degrees. According to my HP-65, the arctangent of 0.25 is 14.03624347 degrees. Close enough for government work. If you *ever* use this information in your ham career, for Pete's sake, let me know! You might want to drop you-know-who a letter about this question, Hi!

22 What's the F.C.C.'s designation for AM television?

A5

23 What type of antenna would you use if you wished to minimize the reception of man-made noise?

Use a *horizontally polarized antenna* (such as a beam or horizontal dipole) because man-made noise is vertically polarized.

24 The operating characteristics of transistors depend quite a bit on what?

The temperature environment in which the transistor is operating at the time.

25 Which of the following figures is correctly portraying a full wave bridge rectifier?

This is a proper illustration:

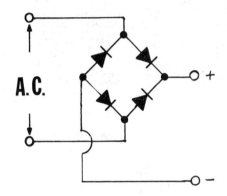

26 An amateur station in repeater operation legally may automatically retransmit what type of signals?

Per 97.126, you can only retransmit radio signals from other amateur radio stations if you're a repeater.

27 Leakage reactance in a transformer causes what?

A decrease in the secondary voltage. Leakage reactance is an unavoidable loss occurring in transformers that prevents the output voltage of the transformer from being *exactly* that which is calculated from the ratio of the primary to secondary windings and the value of the input voltage.

28 What is the output that you can expect from a *balanced modulator?*

Per page 405 in Shrader's (you can order it COD from us if you can't find it elsewhere), the output of the balanced modulator is a double sideband signal with a reduced carrier.

29 The "decibel" is a ratio of output to input power and is a mathematically determined value based on what value of this ratio?

The decibel is *based on the common logarithm of the above ratio.* Huh??? Well, folks, you better know *that* statement! What this is all about is that the decibel value is derived from a formula that goes something like this:

$$\text{Decibel (dB)} = 10 \text{ Log} \frac{\text{output power}}{\text{input power}}$$

If you had to figure this out (and, relax, you won't have to), you'd divide the output power (in watts) by the input power (also in watts). Then you'd enter a table of common logarithms (or use a scientific calculator like the HP-67 or TI-58) and find the logarithm of that division you just did. Lastly, you'd take the logarithm you came up with and multiply it by 10. Now you have the answer in decibels. Wasn't that fun?

Also, you should know that if you double your power it will increase your received signal strength by 3 dB and that one (1) "S" unit (as read on an "S" meter and only below "S 9") is worth about 6 decibels. So, if you were putting *out* 100 watts and attached an amplifier that would raise that to 200 watts, which is exactly double, then the guy on the receiving end would see his "S meter" move up 3 decibels or ½ of an "S" unit (not much, is it?).

30 On which frequencies are A5/F5 (television) emissions permitted in the HF bands for Advanced Class frequencies?

a. 3.800–3.890 MHz   d. 21.270–21.350 MHz
b. 7.150–7.225 MHz   e. 28.500–29.700 MHz
c. 14.200–14.275 MHz

I remember these easily because a. through d. are within the Advanced Class voice frequencies and e. represents frequencies Generals get to use for voice on 10 meters.

31 Given a transformer with an input voltage (primary) of 120 volts and 30 volts out (secondary) with 240 turns on the primary winding, how many turns are on the secondary?

To find this, set up the following equation, with the *voltages on the left side* and windings on the right. Then insert the primary voltage on the top left side of the equation and the secondary voltage on the bottom left. Place the known number of primary turns on the top right and an N (to indicate the *unknown* Number of secondary turns) on the bottom. Notice how the primary voltage (120v) and its associated primary turns (240) are both in the upper portions, or numerators, of the fractions in this equation. To solve for the unknown, cross multiply (30 × 240) and divide by the remaining known value (120) to get 7200 divided by 120. The answer is 60 turns. That was easy!

input voltage (primary) = turns (primary)
output voltage (secondary) = turns (secondary)

$$\frac{120}{30} = \frac{240}{N}$$

$$30 \times 240 = 120 \times N$$

$$\frac{30 \times 240}{120} = N$$

$$\frac{7200}{120} = N$$

$$60 = \text{Number of turns on secondary winding}$$

32 What frequencies are available for repeater operation above 29.5 MHz?

All frequencies are available *except*:

a. 50.0–52.0 MHz	**d. 220.0–220.5 MHz**
b. 144.0–144.5 MHz	**e. 431.0–433.0 MHz**
c. 145.5–146.0 MHz	**f. 435.0–438.0 MHz**

Please note that neither the receive nor the transmit frequency of the repeater may be within these ranges.

33 On what frequencies are A4 emissions (AM facsimile) permitted?

On all ham bands and frequencies from *50.1 MHz* and upwards.

34 The highest frequency that you can operate at which permits radio signals to be transmitted at one point and received at a second, more distant point (beyond the line of sight range and also beyond the normal ground wave range) refracting off the ionosphere is referred to as what?

The Maximum Usable Frequency (MUF)

35 What is meant by "auxiliary operation"?

Radiocommunication for remotely controlling other amateur radio stations, for automatically relaying the radio signals of other amateur radio stations in a system of stations, or for intercommunicating with other amateur stations within a system of amateur radio stations (**WOW!!!**)

36 In what type of circuit would you expect to see a "Zener diode"?

In a voltage regulator circuit.

37 Radioteleprinter signals (RTTY) are transmitted at what different speeds?

They may be transmitted at speeds of 60, 67, 75, or 100 words per minute.

38 What is a reflex klystron used for?

It's used as an oscillator at microwave (about 1.2 gigahertz) frequencies.

39 What's a speech processor used for?

It is used to change (meaning reduce) the peak to average amplitude of the voice signal. As described in the 1981 A.R.L. Handbook on page 12–14, this serves to increase the SSB's average power level.

40 Determine the length of a *quarter-wave* piece of coax whose velocity factor is 0.66 at a frequency of 14.10 MHz.

Use *this* formula:

$$\text{Quarter wavelength in feet} = \frac{\left(\dfrac{984 \times \text{velocity factor}}{\text{frequency in MHz}}\right)}{4}$$

$$\text{Quarter wavelength in feet} = \frac{\left(\dfrac{984 \times 0.66}{14.10}\right)}{4}$$

$$\text{Quarter wavelength in feet} = \frac{\left(\dfrac{649.44}{14.10}\right)}{4}$$

Quarter wavelength in feet = 11.51 feet

To convert your answer to meters, divide the number of feet by 3.2808 (which is the number of feet in one meter).

$$\text{Quarter wavelength in meters} = \frac{11.51}{3.2808}$$

Quarter wavelength in meters = 3.51 meters

Be able to handle these problems with different numbers, so know the formulas. Oh, you would divide by 2 for a half wave length and 1 (or don't divide) for a full wave length. Easy!

41 What is a PIN diode?

This is a light emitting type of diode, principally used above 100 MHz. Consisting of a complex silicon and gold foil (do you know how much gold is selling for now?) the unit has low impedance. When light (or heat) hits the unit (it's not a true diode according to Shrader on p. 172) current can flow and the more light/heat that is applied to the PIN diode, the more current that is permitted to flow.

42 What are the frequencies for F5 emissions?

This question could be asking which of a group of frequencies is valid for transmitting a F5 emission. So, you'll have to know the frequencies. You should also know that F5 and A5 are valid on the same frequencies. I would like to hear from you on the answers to this question. See Question #30 also.

43 In a Colpitts oscillator (they may show you one), what controls the frequency?

The setting of the variable capacitors and the value of the coil. We have not received the exact wording on this, so please send it in.

44 How does the F.C.C. designate "frequency modulated radiotelephony"?

F3 (it would be A3 if they'd asked for "amplitude modulated radiotelephony.")

45 With whom does the U.S. have third party agreements?

The easy way to remember this is that the U.S. has 3rd party agreements with almost all Central and South American countries, Canada, most of the countries of the Caribbean, and only three (3) countries in Africa and the Middle East. We have *no* agreements with the countries of Europe, Asia, or in the Pacific.

46 How many sidebands are produced in the transmission of an FM signal?

An FM signal generates *many* sidebands, the amplitude of which is a function of the amplitude and the frequency of the modulating audio signal. Recall that on AM just two (2) sidebands are produced (upper and lower).

47 Where would you install a *low-pass filter* in order to attenuate (reduce) harmonics?

Between the transmitter *output and the antenna,* or between the final stages and the antenna.

48 One advantage that the Pi-L network has over the Pi network for impedance matching between the final amplifier of a vacuum tube type transmitter and a multiband antenna is what?

The Pi-L network is able to attenuate about 10 dB (or more) of second harmonic energy than your basic Pi network. See page 6–30 of the 1981 ARRL Handbook for schematics.

49 Refer to the following schematic. When the a.c. power source is adjusted to the resonant frequency of the circuit what will happen?

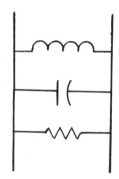

The current flow will be at a maximum because at resonance X_L (inductive reactance from the coil) and X_C (capacitive reactance from the capacitor) cancel each other. Therefore only resistance is left from the little resistor. Even though no numbers are shown, simple inspection will determine that maximum current would flow if you substitute *any* numbers at all.

50 What class of licensee may use SSTV?

A Technician Class, General Class, Advanced Class, or Extra Class licensee. Where he can use SSTV is a function of the class of license, though. So, everyone but a Novice can use SSTV (someplace!).

51 Where would you find a hot carrier diode in a circuit?

In the mixer stages of an HF/VHF/UHF rig.

52 Which of the following figures correctly portrays the frequency response of an M-derived low pass filter?

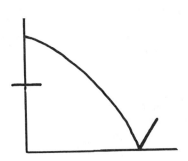

This is it!

53 An amateur radio station may retransmit which of the following?

When properly licensed, it may retransmit the signals of other amateur radio stations.

54 What is the base to emitter voltage of a transistor during normal operation?

It is 0.7 volts. This is all for a silicon transistor because on a germanium transistor it is 0.2–0.3.

55 When is transmitter and antenna information required to be placed in the log of a repeater? - 2 quels.

another standards ?

Whenever (according to 97.103 (e)) your repeater exceeds the height above the average terrain or effective radiated power requirements that are spelled out in 97.67 of the regulations. For example, if your 2 meter repeater antenna height above the average terrain is 75 feet then your ERP cannot exceed 400 watts. If it does then you would have to get special authorization and (when you get it) enter the actual ERP in the log along with the antenna height above the average terrain. I recommend that you read through these regs because there are some subtleties here.

56 What is the proper way to identify your station when using SSTV on 20 meters?

The only legal way to i.d. is by sending the callsigns in CW or by voice. See 97.84 of the Regs.

57 What is intermodulation interference?

It is the interference that transmitter #1 causes to transmitter #2 if the two of them are fairly close together and on the air at the same time. It can cause one of the two (or both) transmitters to transmit a combination of the sum of the two transmitter frequency energies and the difference between the two. The net effect of all of this is interference ending up on other frequencies. Technically, the R.F. energy from 2 or more transmitters in close proximity mix in a final amplifying stage, generating radiated in-band emissions on mathematically related frequencies.

58 What would you do to eliminate intermodulation interference in a repeater?

Insert a *bandpass* filter in the antenna feedline between the transmitter and the antenna. As pointed out in Shrader's (p. 414), you would use a filter that's tuned to the frequency of the offending repeater.

59 How can you improve the signal to noise ratio of your radio?

Use more filtering in the RF stage. I think this is right. Please see page 310 of Shrader's book. Your other choices are: Use a better antenna; more filtering in the AF stage; use a low pass filter. You want in this case to provide additional filtering to the amplification stage because S/N ratio is the ratio of the signal to the power of the noise developed in the amplifier.

60 Which method is *not* a correct means of improving the stability of a drifting VFO?

You *won't* improve the stability of a drifting VFO by increasing the amount of positive feedback in the VFO circuit.

61 What bands (CW and phone) are reserved EXCLUSIVELY for the Extra Class license holder?

You will be told to select which of four (4) frequencies are reserved exclusively for the Extra Class license holder. Here are the exclusive Extra Class frequencies. *Memorize them!!!*

BAND	FREQUENCY RANGE	PHONE/CW
80	3500–3525 kHz	CW
80	3775–3800 kHz	Phone
40	7000–7025 kHz	CW
20	14000–14025 kHz	CW
15	21000–21025 kHz	CW
15	21250–21270 kHz	Phone

They are, *for CW, the first 25 kHz of the 80, 40, 20, and 15 meter bands.* Also, the exclusive phone portions are 25 kHz in the 80 meter band and 20 kHz in the 15 meter band. Maybe that'll help you *memorize* them.

62 What is the relationship between an unmodulated signal and one which is 100% modulated?

An unmodulated signal's power will increase by 50% of its unmodulated value when the signal is 100% modulated. For example, an unmodulated signal of 200 watts will increase to 300 watts when that same signal is modulated to 100%.

63 Refer to the schematic shown below and determine the voltage rating of the Zener diode.

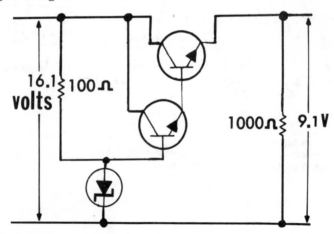

The answer is 10.5 volts. Find this by adding the output voltage (9.1) to the base-to-emitter voltage of each transistor (0.7). This gives you 9.1 + 0.7 + 0.7 = 10.5 volts. If the input and output values change, the method of solving this remains the same, so know the methodology!

64 What does *"transistor saturation"* mean?

To begin with, the word "transistor" is a bit misleading since the effect of saturation applies to *both* tubes and transistors. Saturation occurs *in an amplifier* when the tube/transistor is unable to put out *additional* current when the input to the amplifier is increased. Output normally increases when the input is increased, but only up to a certain point, and *that* point is called "saturation". Refer to the following diagram for a pictorial presentation. This diagram is *not* on the test, by the way.

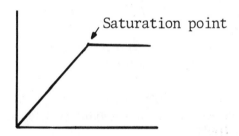

65 At what speed do radio waves travel?

That depends on what they're traveling through. They move a lot slower through the mud in the Everglades swamp than through a copper wire. The point that I'm trying to make is that the speed at which radio waves travel depends on the density of the medium through which they pass. In a *vacuum* they travel at about 186,000 miles per second, but through anything else, they move slower.

66 What is the formula for finding the total capacitance of two (2) capacitors in SERIES?

The total capacitance of two capacitors in series is *equal to the product of the two capacitors divided by the sum of the two capacitors.* By the way, this is the way the answer goes on the actual exam. The conventional presentation of the formula isn't used, so *know the wording!!!*

67 What can be done to avoid generating excessive harmonics? This is a *favorite* question of the F.C.C.

All of the following are correct, but only one of these will show up as the correct choice on your test:

　　a. **Use high "Q" circuits.**
　　b. **Use the minimum possible grid bias.**
　　c. **Use an antenna tuner (may be called a "tuned antenna coupler") between the transmitter *output* of the rig and the transmission line/coax.**
　　d. ***Shield all of the RF amplifier stages (not the transmitter itself!).***
　　e. ***Use the lowest amount of grid drive that's necessary to get the desired output from the rig.***

68 In the 40 meter band, what frequency range is reserved exclusively for the Extra and Advanced Class license holders?

7.150–7.225 MHz.

69 If you overmodulate, what effect can this have on your power output?

It can result in no RF output part of the time.

70 If you overmodulate, you may create spurious sidebands. What is another name for these spurious sidebands?

Splatter.

71 How would you control TVI?

Install a high-pass filter on the TV (at the TV's antenna terminals). Don't you dare choose "install a low-pass filter on the *receiver.*" For Pete's sake, read carefully!

72 Refer to the schematic below and determine the phase angle from the given information.

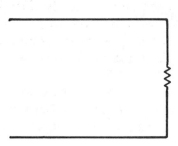

The phase angle is *zero degrees!!!* This is because it's a resistive circuit, folks, and there has to be some reactance in there to generate a phase angle greater than zero degrees.

COMMENT . . .

I am waiting for the F.C.C. to hit us with some more questions on "specialized communications," such as more slow-scan T.V. questions or ones on moon bounce or RTTY. Keep an eye out for these and let me know A.S.A.P. if they show up.

If you object to any question or questions on the actual exam, you are urged to write Mr. Jay Jackson at the F.C.C. and tell him your feelings. His address is:

> Mr. Jay Jackson
> Personal Radio Branch
> Federal Communications Commission
> Washington, D.C. 20554
> Telephone: (202) 254-6884

Mr. Jackson has the unenviable position of writing the tests. You must tell him what the exam number is. For example, 4A-76-0780-BE. Also tell him the question number and explain why you take exception to it. Believe it or not, he'll respond by changing the particular question if sufficient people squawk it. Jay wants to see a good exam and your comments are welcomed by him. Send us a copy of your letter.

73 According to F.C.C. regulation 97.93, you may not transmit a carrier wave unless modulated for the purpose of communication, except for brief tests or adjustments or single audio frequency tones for the purpose of short duration tests below a certain frequency. What is the frequency that is specified in the F.C.C. regulations?

51 megahertz. This regulation ties in with the definition of an AØ emission. Watch out for this question! You should know that there are frequencies (all amateur frequencies above 51.0 MHz) where you can make AØ emissions for as long as you wish without *any* limitation.

74 Where may AØ emissions (non-modulated carrier) be used *without any limitations* as to the duration of the transmission?

From 51.0 MHz and upwards. Below 51.0 MHz, the signal must be limited to short periods of time.

75 Refer to the diagram below. What does this circuit represent?

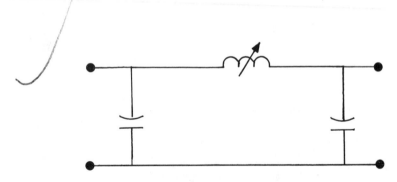

This is an "M-derived π section" *low-pass filter*. On the exam, it will probably be called just a low-pass filter. Note that a low-pass filter has vertical capacitors and a horizontal coil. This particular type of low-pass filter has a tuned coil in it instead of just a simple coil but, for our purposes, it doesn't matter. The *key* to identifying it as a low-pass filter is the pair of *vertical capacitors*.

25

76 What is the resonant frequency of the circuit shown below?

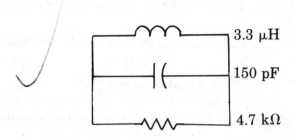

3.3 μH

150 pF

4.7 kΩ

To find this, we use the following formula:

$$\text{Resonant frequency (in kHz)} = \frac{1{,}000{,}000}{2\,\pi\,\sqrt{LC}}$$

Where π = 3.14
L = inductance, in μH
C = capacitance, in pF

You're going to need to buy/beg/borrow/steal a calculator that'll handle square roots or get slick with a slide rule again (ugh!). Be sure the calculator can handle all the digits you'll need!!!

$$\text{Frequency (in kHz)} = \frac{1{,}000{,}000}{2 \times 3.14 \times \sqrt{3.3 \times 150}}$$

$$\text{Frequency (in kHz)} = \frac{1{,}000{,}000}{6.28 \times \sqrt{495.0}}$$

$$\text{Frequency (in kHz)} = \frac{1{,}000{,}000}{6.28 \times 22.248595}$$

$$\text{Frequency (in kHz)} = \frac{1{,}000{,}000}{139.72118}$$

Frequency (in kHz) = 7157.111 kHz (or 7.15 MHz)

77 Which of the following statements about radio waves is *false?*

"Radio waves always travel at the speed of light." Make damn sure you carefully read the questions on the exam.

78 What is "ducting" and which portion of the frequency spectrum does it affect?

"Ducting" is *a type of propagation that occurs in the VHF and UHF regions.* Ducting works in conjunction with super-refraction, in that a radio signal will undergo repeated refractive cycles in an area between two ionized layers before returning to the earth. It is somewhat common on 2 meters and more so on the higher frequencies. Contacts between Hawaii and California have occurred on 70 cm (435 MHz) utilizing this effect. See page 489 of Shrader's for additional details. It typically occurs during an inversion.

79 What class amplifier should be used in the final stage of an SSB transmitter?

A Class AB_1 amplifier.

80 There are AC currents in a transformer which come from the primary stage of the transformer and heat up the core. The heating of the transformer's core causes a loss. What's the name of the AC currents which cause this loss?

Eddy currents.

81 Losses in a transformer due to *eddy currents* may be reduced by doing what?

Laminating the core (cutting it into very thin strips) and then insulating these strips from each other by applying either shellac or varnish to them.

82 Transformer losses due to AC passing through the intense magnetic fields found in the windings of metallic core transformers is termed what?

Hysteresis.

83 What type of propagation would be represented by RF travelling between layers of air?

Ducting.

84 How is station identification accomplished when you are using radioteletype (RTTY)?

By using *radiotelegraphy* (that is how the F.C.C. refers to CW) to identify your station *every ten (10) minutes.* You may also identify by voice (in English).

85 What is "aurora"?

This refers to the ionization of our atmosphere in the area of the magnetic poles by ionized particles coming from the sun. This ionization creates an effect called "auroral flutter," which is typified by a *rapidly* fluctuating signal strength. The frequencies affected by this are those from about 28 MHz and upwards from there.

86 How are signals affected by auroral disturbances?

They are subject to rapid fluttering. The fluttering tends to make it easier to copy CW signals than SSB signals. In order to make voice communications readable, additional (and significant) amounts of powers must be used, especially when higher frequencies are worked. See page 21 of *The ARRL Antenna Book* for additional explanation.

87 What is one of the results of auroral disturbances?

You will find that HF communications are disrupted and that VHF communications are improved.

88 With respect to a station being operated by remote control (meaning a repeater), provisions must be incorporated to limit transmission to a period of no more than a certain period of time after a *malfunction* in the control link. How long is that time span?

Three minutes.

89 How many *harmonics* are there in a square wave signal?

An infinite number of *odd* harmonics.

90 If you have three capacitors in parallel, and the first is a 200 pF capacitor and the second one is a 170 pF capacitor, what would the value of the third one be if the *total* capacitance was 520 pF?

The formula for finding total capacitance is:
$$C_{total} = C1 + C2 + C3$$

You have been given C_{total}, C1, and C2 and are being asked to find C3, in effect. So, we transpose the formula like so:
$$C3 = C_{total} - (C1 + C2)$$
$$C3 = 520\ pF - (200\ pF + 170\ pF)$$
$$C3 = 520\ pF - 370\ pF$$
$$C3 = 150\ pF$$

91 With what other stations may a station in auxiliary operation communicate?

Only with those stations that are shown in the system network diagram, per 97.86 (c) of the regulations.

92 How do you mathematically figure the shape factor of a crystal lattice filter?

Measure the bandwidth at the −60 dB point on the selectivity curve (in kHz) and divide that value by the bandwidth value at the −6 dB point. The *most selective filter*, which is what the F.C.C. is looking for, is the one which has the lowest shape factor. For example, a shape factor of 1.60 is *better* than one with a shape factor of 1.67. So, in this case, you'd choose the answer that works out to a shape factor of 1.60. It's also possible to define this using the −60dB and −3dB points.

93 A good quality crystal lattice band-pass type of filter for use in a single sideband radio would probably use which of the following bandwidths?

    A. 400 Hz at −6dB and 700 Hz at −60dB.
    B. 2.5 kHz at −6dB and 4.0 kHz at −60dB.
    C. 6.0 kHz at −6dB and 12.0 kHz at −60dB.
    D. 300 Hz at −6dB and 3000 Hz at −60dB.

To solve this, divide the −60dB value by the −6dB value. This will give you the "shape factor." The lowest value of shape factor is the desired one (in general). The shape factor for "A" is 1.75, for "B" it's 1.60, for "C" it's 2.0, and for "D" it's 10.0. However, if you are aware that a filter for voice needs a −6dB bandwidth of about 3 kHz then it's easy to see that the right anwer is "B."

94 The *shape factor* of a crystal lattice filter can never be less than what value?

The value cannot be less than 1.0 *ever!*

95 Why would an amateur use traps on a horizontal dipole?

To permit the use of a single feedline to obtain multi-band operation.

96 If you allow your amateur radio license to expire, you may apply for renewal during the grace period following the date of expiration. How long is the grace period that is provided by 97.13 (d)?

The grace period is 5 years. The grace period used to be one year, but was changed to five years in March 1979.

97 What is a major *disadvantage* of the transistor?

It cannot dissipate large amounts of heat at the collector-base junction.

98 The "true horizon" or "geometric horizon" is the actual horizon that you can see, and its distance from you is a function of how high you are above the Earth's surface. However, VHF and UHF signals may be transmitted *beyond the true horizon* due to bending of the radio signal within the troposphere (between sea level and roughly 36,000 feet above sea level). The signals reach the Earth at a point called the "radio path horizon." How far is this beyond the true horizon?

What a lot of verbiage! Anyway, the radio path horizon is about 33% (or ⅓) beyond the true horizon.

99 Calculate the length in feet of a half-wave dipole at 7.150 MHz.

Using $\dfrac{468}{f(MHz)}$ as the formula, you get 65.45 feet.

100 What's the normal bandwidth of a single sideband filter?

The normal bandwidth is 2.4 kHz.

101 What type of propagation would a repeater station use?

Space wave.

102 An amateur station used solely for the purpose of controlling a remote control model is limited to what amount of output power and how is the unit labelled?

It is limited to one (1) watt (*not kilowatt*) and a plate or an I.D. card must be attached to the unit indicating your call sign and your name and address. This is per F.C.C. regulation 97.99.

103 What is a bandpass filter?

A bandpass filter is a filter designed to pass a certain segment of the spectrum or a block of frequencies and reject everything above and below that block of frequencies. Here is the frequency response curve of a typical bandpass filter:

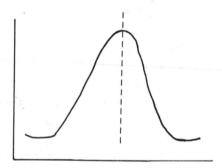

104 Where are A1 emissions permitted?

On all amateur frequencies.

105 What is the half power bandwidth (0.7071 relative response) of a parallel resonant circuit (see the circuit below) with a resonant frequency of 12.800 MHz and a Q of 218?

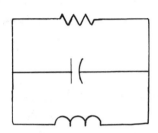

I shall refer to the book *Electronic Communication* by Robert L. Shrader. (See our Recommended Book List at the back of this manual. If you don't have this book, then you're hurting when it comes to an excellent reference book.) Shrader points out that we sometimes need a bandpass filter and it behooves us to know how wide a band of frequencies that the thing is passing. Well, you need some kind of standard for this and it turns out that the standard is one that you and I don't get to see often but is one used by Collins (for example). What we do is measure how wide the band is at a point which is roughly 70% of the maximum voltage/current. It turns out that this is called (see Shrader's for the "why") the −3 dB point. We are used to seeing −6 dB. As the French say, "c'est la vie." Anyway, the narrower the bandwidth is at this point (or even our −6 dB point) the sharper the filtering action is. You can get this bandwidth narrower by using a higher Q circuit (you get higher Q by using higher quality/higher tolerances/ higher cost components). So, once you have the frequency at which you wish to measure the bandwidth, then you use the following easy formula.

The tricky thing you have to remember here is that the resonant frequency MUST BE IN KILOHERTZ for the formula to work right. So, 12.800 MHz is equal to 12,800 kHz and makes our formula look like this when we plug in the values:

$$\text{Bandwidth (kHz)} = \frac{\text{Resonant frequency (kHz)}}{\text{Q of circuit}}$$

$$\text{Bandwidth (kHz)} = \frac{12800 \text{ kHz}}{218}$$

$$\text{Bandwidth (kHz)} = 58.71559633 \text{ kHz}$$

The F.C.C. would call this 59 kHz on your test. To show you how easy it is to pick the right answer once you have done the proper math, it is interesting to note that the other reported choices are 37, 16, and 6. Thus the F.C.C. has helped you by having no answer even close to the correct one.

106 If you wished to take advantage of auroral disturbances, where would you direct your antenna?

You would point it toward the pole (in the northern hemisphere, that means turn your antenna toward the North Pole). The antennas of both the receiving and the transmitting station would have to be pointed towards the pole.

107 What is the relationship between your position relative to the Equator and auroral propagation?

As is pointed out in the A.R.R.L. Antenna Book on page 21, the propagation is NONEXISTANT IN THE TROPICS (meaning near the Equator) and is more pronounced the closer you get to the poles. Under the conditions we had in the interior of Alaska, the auroral propagation was tremendous!

108 A control operator must be what?

A licensed amateur operator.

109 What indication do you have that the SWR on the line is high?

You have to retune after making very small changes in frequency.

110 If you have a 70 ohm ½ wave antenna to be matched to a 50 ohm transmission line with a quarter wave matching section, what value in ohms should the matching section be?

We find the proper way to solve this is to multiply the two ohmages together (70 × 50 = 3500) and take the square root of the product ($\sqrt{3500}$ = 59.16079783) to get the answer.

111 What is the voltage and current on a light emitting diode (LED)?

It is 1½ to 2 volts and 10 to 20 milliamps for a *red* LED.

112 Which of the following is true regarding FM sidebands?

They are mirror images of each other.

113 A single sideband transmitter has an average power of 1 kilowatt. What is its peak envelope power (PEP)?

1.41 K.W.'s. This is found by dividing the average power by 0.707 to get PEP.

114 If a repeater has an output power of 75 watts, an antenna with 10dB gain over isotropic, a 3 dB loss in the feedline, and a 4 dB loss in the duplexers, what is the effective radiated power (ERP)?

Solve this by taking 10 dB and subtracting from it the 4 dB loss in the feedline and the 3 dB loss in the duplexers. This gives you 3 dB (which means a doubling of power). Then double the 75 watts and you get an answer of 150. Piece of cake! Now try it with a 7 dB gain in the antenna with the same feedline and duplexer losses. You should get an ERP of 75 watts.

115 Given a collector current of 10 milliamperes and a base current of .10 mA, what is the beta of this transistor?

Recall that "beta" is the ratio of the collector current to the base current. This is mathematically presented by dividing the collector current (10) by the base current (.10) and getting an answer of *100*. That, gentle reader, is the answer that Uncle Charley is looking for today!

116 Define the "alpha cutoff" frequency of a transistor.

It's the frequency at which the current gain of your common base circuit drops down to 0.707 (remember *Boeing 707*), which is 3 dB down, of the gain at 1000 Hz. The alpha cutoff frequency determines the highest operating frequency of a transistor amplifier.

117 List some of the advantages of the transistor over a tube.

a. The transistor is much more efficient because it does not waste power by dissipating heat.
b. The transistor takes up very little space.
c. The transistor is generally cheaper than the tube.
d. The transistor can handle more jarring and vibration than a tube, making it much more rugged and reliable.
e. The transistor's housing is not nearly as fragile as the tube's glass envelope (which goes along with being more rugged).
f. The transistor does not require heater and plate voltages, resulting in smaller power supplies and also in lower DC voltages within the circuit.
g. The transistor has a lower impedance than a tube, which can, among other things, eliminate the transformer in a properly designed transistor amplifier circuit.

118 Filtering and phasing are two different methods of accomplishing what?

Suppression of the undesired sideband in A3 emissions.

119 The FM equivalent of "over-modulation" is excessive frequency deviation. The regulations specify that on frequencies below 52.5 MHz, the bandwidth of F3 emissions (that's F.C.C. talk for what we call FM) may not exceed what value?

The regulations (97.65) say that F3 emissions may not exceed the bandwidth of A3 emissions (AM to us), which are, in turn, limited to 3 kHz for SSB transmissions.

120 What is "skin effect?"

Skin effect is an AC (*not* DC) phenomenon. As the frequency is increased, the electrons will tend to travel on the surface of the conductor. By the way, this effect causes an increase in the resistance of the conductor.

121 What is the maximum power to be used during satellite communications?

Do not exceed 100 (*not* 10) watts *effective radiated power.*

122 The elevation angle of an antenna used in satellite communications should be set to approximately what angle of tilt?

Set it to approximately 30° (*not* 15°).

123 What are F1 emissions?

This is frequency shift keying (FSK) and is the "regular" teletype that we hear in the CW portions of the HF bands. F1 emissions aren't permitted in the voice portions of the bands but can be *used in the CW only portions.* Here they are. Memorize the first five (a—e).

a. 3.525–3.775 MHz   f. 50.1–54.0 MHz
b. 7.025–7.150 MHz   g. 144.1–148.0 MHz
c. 14.025–14.200 MHz   h. 220–225 MHz
d. 21.025–21.250 MHz   i. 420–450 MHz
e. 28.000–28.500 MHz   j. 1215–1300 MHz

124 When do you *not* use "Q" signals?

During voice (A3/F3) transmissions. Remember that "Q" signals are intended *only* for CW use.

125 What is the "beta" of a transistor?

It's the ratio of the collector current to the base current.

126 What characteristic of a crystal *principally* determines its frequency at resonance?

The dimensions of the crystal. May have "thickness" or "size" instead of dimensions.

127 When must a detailed written description of the repeater circuit and installation data be given to the F.C.C.?

Whenever the antenna height and/or effective radiated power (e.r.p.) exceeds the limits specified in 97.67 (c).

128 What is meant by the term *radiation resistance* as it applies to antennas?

***It is an assumed resistance, which, if present, would dissipate the energy that is actually radiated by the antenna.* On page 492 of Shrader, it is pointed out that you could mathematically determine this value easily if you knew the current and radiated power in an antenna system by using the formula $R = P \div I^2$. We can describe this as being the radiated power of an antenna divided by the square of the current at the antenna input.**

129 With respect to FM transmissions, what is "frequency deviation?"

It is a deviation of the carrier frequency (from a center frequency) that is proportional to the amplitude of the modulating signal. Among hams it is sometimes referred to as "carrier swing."

130 What is the definition of "modulation index?"

It is the ratio of the deviation of the FM carrier signal to the modulating frequency. The modulation index is also known as the deviation ratio.

131 Given a frequency deviation of 2700 Hertz under the influence of a 900 Hertz tone, what would the *Modulation Index* be?

Recall that the modulation index is the result of dividing the frequency deviation by the modulating frequency. Here we have a frequency deviation of 2700 Hz divided by the modulating frequency of 900 Hz. This gives us a *modulation index of 3.0.* Note that if we had used a frequency deviation of 3000 Hz and a 1000 Hz tone, it *still* would give us a modulation index of 3. Modulation index is important because *the number of FM sidebands* and the bandwidth are both related to the modulation index. See page 453 of Shrader's book for more information on this and the previous two questions. This is a super book and better than 90% of the texts written for amateurs. You can order the book from us, get it at your bookstore, or perhaps find it in the technical section of your junior college bookstore. It's worth every penny it costs. Besides, you want to understand some of this, don't you? Well, Shrader's book explains it better than most, so get it and I can promise you that it will be the most used book in your ham library.

132 What is true power?

The amount of power that can be lost in the form of heat. We can calculate this by the formula $P = I^2R$ or by $P = E^2 \div R$. What you *must* know is that true power is measured in watts.

133 In a resonant circuit, what is the relationship between capacitive and inductive reactance?

They are the same $(X = X_c = X_L)$. This defines "resonance."

134 Which of the following is the designation for radiotelephony?

On the exam it is reported to be F3. This is what you and I call FM voice.

135 Refer to the following circuits. What components values are required in schematic B in order to produce an output that is identical to the voltage drop across the lower 10,000 ohms resistor in schematic A?

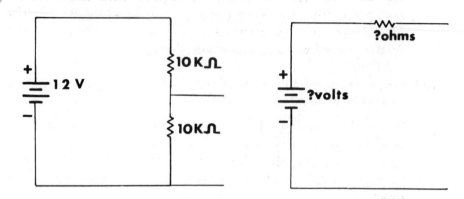

The answer is 6 volts and 5000 ohms and is found by simply using a thing called Thevenin's Theorem (thought you'd get a jolt out of that!). Basically, we are going to use 6 volts for the voltage required. We can do this because the voltage drops across each of the resistors are the same because the resistors have identical values. Simple observation tells us that together both of the resistors will dissipate 12 volts so each one must dissipate 6 volts each. That takes care of the voltage. The resistance is found by taking the two resistors in parallel ($R_1 \times R_2) \div (R_1 + R_2$). If you will do the math you'll get an answer of 5,000 ohms. Thus we see our hero riding off into the sunset with 6 volts and 5000 ohms tucked under his arm. Piece of cake!

136 If the resistors in the above circuit "A" are changed to 20kΩ resistors, what battery voltage and resistance will produce a circuit with exactly the same voltage and current characteristics, as measured at the "+" and "−" terminals?

6 volts and 10,000 ohms. Perhaps an easier way for you to solve this type of problem is to take half the value of the schematic "A" voltage and half the value of one of the resistors.

137 How are HF signals affected by sudden ionospheric disturbances?

According to page 21 of the A.R.R.L. Antenna Book, the
HF signals will suddenly disappear and then slowly
reappear. To reappear back to the level at which the
signals were before the disturbances began may take
from several minutes to several hours.

138 Where is the best place to place a loading coil in a shortened
vertical antenna?

Near the top of the antenna. It is inconsequential
whether you place it in the base (meaning bottom load
it) or in the middle. The effect is about the same. However, top loading of an antenna is better than middle or
base loading.

139 When does the maximum power go to the antenna?

When the load (meaning the antenna's impedance)
matches the source (meaning the line impedance). This
results in a standing wave ratio of 1:1.

140 What is the proper operating procedure when using SSTV?

Reduce the power to less than that used during SSB
voice operations. This is because there is a 100% duty
cycle in use during the transmission of an SSTV signal
(like a RTTY signal in that respect). SSTV signals have
a lower peak-to-average ratio than voice signals.

141 The controlling frequency of a repeater shall be what?

According to 97.88 (e) of the regulations, "a station in
repeater operation shall be operated by radio remote
control only when the control link uses frequencies
other than the input (receiving) frequencies of the station in repeater operation." I regret to inform you that
this is another one of those questions that folks can
remember the question but none of the answers. So, you
should know the above and also be aware of where you
can and cannot use a repeater on certain frequencies.

142 Whenever the alternating sine-wave voltage and current in a circuit are out of phase, true power amounts to what?

As pointed out in Shrader on p. 106, true power is equal to I^2R and is always less than the product of the voltage and current magnitudes (which is the definition of apparent power).

143 What is reactive power?

It is the power calculated by multiplying volts times amps (apparent power) and then trapped within the coils and capacitors of a pure reactive circuit. It causes an illusion of a power loss when there really isn't one. A power loss has to be reflected by some evidence of heat. There is no heat generated here. Reactive power requires magnetic fields to be present and these fields "hold back" the actual work that the circuit can do. It is, therefore, *the result of electrical energy being stored in electrostatic or electromagnetic fields.* Too much reactive power is a bad thing because it can do no useful work. Useful work is measured in watts, not volt-amps.

144 What does the first *mixer* stage in a double conversion superhetrodyne receiver do?

Briefly, it produces the intermediate frequency. As pointed out earlier, in the mixer the tuned in signal is hetrodyned with the output of the local oscillator. The results are the sum of the two frequencies and the difference between the two frequencies. The difference is often 455 kHz and is called the intermediate frequency. There is no amplification in a mixer.

145 What's the purpose of the 1st *i.f.* stage in a double conversion superhetrodyne receiver?

As pointed out on page 437 of ELECTRONIC COMMUNICATION by Robert L. Shrader (4th edition—published in 1980 by McGraw-Hill), the purpose is to reject the image of the desired frequency. It is important to note, also, that the 2nd i.f. is used to narrow the passband. The details for this are on page 429 of Shrader's.

146 Antenna impedance is matched when?

There are a number of correct ways to describe this. You'd better know them all. We could say when the resistance of the load is equal to the impedance of the transmission line. It can also be termed as being the condition when resistance and reactance of the load equal the input resistance. According to page 19-2 of the 1981 Handbook by the A.R.R.L., you may say that the matching occurs when you have the impedance of the load equal to the impedance of the line. Understand and appreciate that impedance is made up of resistance and reactance. Don't pick any answer containing the reference to inductance.

147 Using a single tone test on a SSB amplifer operating AB_1, how does the average power input compare to the PEP that is produced by the amplifier?

Gads!!! Well, this single tone business is the same thing as holding the key down during CW operations. The average power and the PEP of a CW signal are identical. For CW, the maximum power input is 1000 watts PEP (which, *for CW only*, is the same as *average* power) while it's 2000 watts PEP for SSB (which is *not* the same as an *average* input power of 2000 watts).

148 How do you make chocolate cake?

This isn't really on the test but if you don't find making chocolate cake complicated then passing this test will be a breeze. I want you cooks to relax and study this stuff like a recipe. Also, you may send your culinary accomplishments as relate to this question to us instead of Washington. We have the "taste" to appreciate your efforts (who said ham radio wasn't fun?).

149 Refer to the schematic shown below. What is the voltage between points B and A?

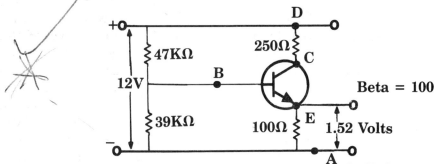

Here's the solution for the entire circuit and all the associated values.

a. Assume that the *currents* across the emitter and collector resistors are the same.

b. Determine the current on the emitter resistor (I = E/R or I = 1.52 volts/100 ohms) and it's .0152 amps.

c. Using a current of 0.0152 amps, determine the voltage across the collector's resistor by using the formula E = I * R. (E = .0152 × 250 = 3.8000000 volts). You now have the voltage across the emitter resistor (E to A voltage = 1.52) and the voltage across the collector resistor (D to C voltage = 3.80 volts). You must now know from birth or something that the base to emitter voltage (B to E on the schematic) is 0.7 volts. Now, our last voltage determination will be the base to collector voltage (B to C). This is found by knowing that it is the difference between the D to A voltage (12) and the sum of the three voltages we have already mentioned. Thus we get: B to C voltage = 12 volts − (1.52 + 3.80 + 0.7). This comes out to: B to C voltage = 12 − 6.02 = 5.98 volts. Now we draw the following box and put our values in the appropriate section. You'll see that 1.52 is in the bottom section between the lines marked E and A and on the schematic there are 1.52 volts between points E and A.

	You and Me	FCC
D		
	3.80	3.76
C		
	5.98	6.01
B		
	0.7	0.7
E		
	1.52	1.52
A		

d. Note that the F.C.C. uses 3.76 for D to C. You too would get this answer if you performed the 3 pages of math necessary for this and did your calculations based on the beta. I do not find many folks comfortable with that, so we do it simpler but less accurately. Now the F.C.C. will ask you for the voltage between D and B. That's the sum of D to C plus C to B (3.80 + 5.98 = 9.78). The F.C.C. answer is 9.77. Also you may be asked what the voltage is between B and A. This is the sum of B to E and E to A (0.7 + 1.52 = 2.22 volts). The F.C.C. answer is 2.2 volts. Lastly you may be asked for the voltage between C and A. It's the sum of C to B plus and E to A, or (using our numbers and not the F.C.C.'s) it's the sum of 5.98 + 0.7 + 1.52 or 8.20 volts. The F.C.C.'s answer is 8.24 and the other three choices are all starting with a 3, so it's easy to pick out the right answer. *Know how to solve this circuit* so you can get the right answer if the values are changed.

150 Which frequency bands are available for auxiliary operation?

It's everything above 220.5 MHz except two sections in the 70 centimeter band. You CANNOT use 431–433 MHz or 435–438 MHz or 220.0–220.5 MHz. You had better know what you cannot use because they're on the test as choices! Please see 97.61 (d) of the regulations for all of the details on this and get to know this well.

151 What are the formulas for calculating the reactance of a capacitor and also for a coil? *MEMORIZE THESE!*

For calculating the capacitive reactance of a capacitor use:

$$X_c = \frac{1}{2\pi fC}$$

Xc = **Capacitive reactance**
π = **3.14 (use *no* other value)**
f = **Frequency (given)**
C = **Capacitance**

For calculating the inductive reactance of a coil use:

$$X_L = 2\pi fL$$

X_L = **Inductive reactance**
π = **3.14**
f = **Frequency**
L = **Coil's inductance**

152 If you had a square wave on an oscilloscope it would represent what?

The sine wave (or fundamental frequency) plus all the odd harmonics (3rd, 5th, 7th, etc.).

153 If you had a sawtooth wave on an oscilloscope, what would it represent?

It would be composed of the sine wave (or fundamental frequency) plus all of the odd harmonics (meaning the 3rd, 5th, 7th, etc.) and the even harmonics (meaning the 2nd, 4th, 6th, etc). Another way they might phrase this is to say that a sawtooth wave is composed of the fundamental frequency plus all of the odd and even harmonics. Please see page 3.22 and 3.23 of Bill Orr's Radio Handbook for more details.

154 A silicon controlled rectifier (S.C.R.) has the electrical characteristics of what other component? *open*

A silicon controlled rectifier acts like a *switch*.

155 What does the term "Q" of a *component* (*not* the circuit) mean?

This refers to the quality of a circuit containing resistance and reactance (either inductive or capacitive). As the term applies to coils, the higher the value of the Q of a coil, the lower the internal resistance in the *coil*. In a coil, you find the value of Q by doing this:

$$Q = \frac{2\pi fL}{R}$$

In a capacitor, Q is the ratio of the capacitive reactance to the resistance. The formula for Q in a *capacitor* is:

$$Q = \frac{Xc}{R} = \frac{1}{2\pi fCR}$$

We can see that by increasing the frequency we reduce the Q in a capacitor but it is just the opposite in a coil. On the other hand we know that a circuit consists of components other than a single coil or capacitor. It becomes necessary then to be able to calculate the Q of a circuit that's series as well as one that's parallel. The formulas are just the opposite of each other, so get comfortable with them *before* you take the test because you could be asked to use either one.

$$Q_{series} = \frac{\text{Reactance of coil or capacitor at resonance}}{\text{Total series resistance}}$$

$$Q_{parallel} = \frac{\text{Total parallel resistance}}{\text{Reactance of coil or capacitor at resonance}}$$

156 Determine the Q of the schematic shown below at a frequency of 14.128 MHz.

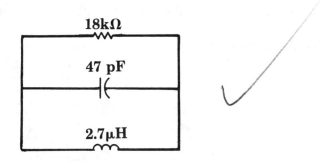

18kΩ

47 pF

2.7μH

We will use this formula from p. 131 of Shrader's:

$$Q = \frac{\text{Resistance in ohms}}{\sqrt{L/C}}$$

Where R = Resistance, in ohms
L = Inductance, in microhenrys
C = Capacitance, in microfarads

Note: To change picofarads to microfarads, divide 47 picofarads by 1,000,000 and you'll get 0.000047 microfarads.

$$Q = \frac{18,000}{\sqrt{2.7/0.000047}}$$

$$Q = \frac{18,000}{\sqrt{57446.80851}}$$

$$Q = \frac{18,000}{239.6806386}$$

$$Q = 75.099933410$$

157 If you increase the power of a unit 10 times, what is the decibel increase?

You increase it by 10 decibels. This is found by using this formula:

$$dB = 10 \log \frac{\text{final power}}{\text{initial power}}$$

Let's say you start out with 100 watts and increase it 10 times to 1000 watts. You would divide 1000 by 100 and then take the logarithm of that number. At this point you need a scientific calculator. The log of 1000/100 is the same as saying the log of 10. The log of 10 turns out to be 1. Multiply this by 10 and you get an answer of 10 dB. Based on 6 dB to the S unit, that's about 1.67 S units increase. Now that's all the other guy would hear if I put a linear on my Kenwood TS-180S. Doesn't make sense to spend the money when I can get 8 dB or so gain from my Hy-Gain TH3MK3. Thus, if you want to get the best ratio of dollars to decibels then put your bucks into the antenna. Did you know that you can get as much as 15 dB from a log periodic? That's more efficient than a full gallon linear to my way of thinking (although a linear doesn't take up the room that a log periodic does). Anyway, the point is that you are smarter to initially put your money and your time into your antenna system. Once you get it set up so as to give you every drop you can squeeze out of it then you might consider a linear. I sometimes wonder if perhaps we haven't gone too far with this linear business. It sometimes seems like we're just trying to shout each other down like our 11 meter colleagues. Makes you pause and think, doesn't it? Wonder if they'll restrict power of the new W.A.R.C. awarded bands? It would be a nice change.

158 Which of the following 95 things will *NOT* help you during moonbounce or Earth-Moon-Earth (EME) communications?

Having a horizontally polarized antenna won't help to my way of thinking because of things like the Faraday effect, etc.

159 On which of the following 4,273 frequency choices may an Advanced Class licensee legally operate?

You may operate on 14.235 megahertz using a variety of emission types, including A1, A3, and A5. Better know your frequencies!

160 Tell me all there is to know about hot carrier diodes!

Greetings from the Extra Class exams (because, gentle reader, that's where the 3 questions on this subject come from)! Hot carrier diodes are utilized as detectors and mixers that are working in the HF/VHF/UHF frequency ranges. They are fast acting diodes and, as pointed out in the 1981 edition of the A.R.R.L. HANDBOOK on page 4–10, have several advantages over point contact diodes. Hot carrier diodes are also called "Schottky" diodes.

161 The signal-to-noise ratio in a 2 meter/220 MHz/440 MHz rig is primarily determined by noise that is generated where?

In the IF stages. This is why you want VHF equipment to have the lowest possible noise figure.

162 What's the relationship between a dipole and its height above the ground?

Decreasing the height will increase the angle of radiation while *increasing the height will decrease its angle of radiation or decrease the vertical lobes, which will make it more directional.*

163 If you raise a dipole's height above the ground, what effect does this have?

It *decreases the vertical lobes!* It also increases the horizontal lobes (not on test), which makes the dipole more directional and reduces the angle of radiation.

164 If the height of a vertical trap antenna above the ground is raised, what happens?

The angle of radiation of the main lobe is smaller.

Achtung Computer Freaks:
Hey, we are in desperate need of really, really slick, colorful, easy-to-operate at the end-user level programs for the Apple II Plus. I want somebody to send me a red-hot word processing program. I'm also looking for super duper ham programs. They must be on disc and based on either DOS 3.2.1 or 3.3 (we prefer DOS 3.2.1). If what you've got is truly fantastic and marketable (and different), then maybe we can peddle it for you. Send all submissions via Certified Mail—Return Receipt Requested. Gracias!

165 How can I ever remember all of those different emission designations the F.C.C. uses?

Perhaps an example of each one will help:

AØ Unmodulated carrier wave. Just like holding the CW key down and not letting up.

A1 This is the normal telegraphy or CW that we use.

A2 A special kind of teletype that is used only in the VHF bands from 50.1 MHz and upwards.

A3 AM, SSB, and DSB *voice.*

A4 Facsimile. Used only from 50.1 MHz and upwards.

A5 Fast *and* slow-scan television. Fast-scan is UHF and slow-scan is used principally in the HF regions.

FØ Same as AØ for all intents and purposes.

F1 This is the teletype that you hear in the CW portion of the HF bands.

F2 Touchtone keying. Like what is used on 2 meter gear and on your telephone. Applies only to frequencies from 50.1 MHz and upwards.

F3 Common *FM voice.*

F4 Facsimile (but this time it's FM facsimile. The A4 is AM). Used only *from 220 MHz and upwards.*

F5 Frequency modulated television. Don't think you'll find much of this in the United States.

166 In an 80 meter/40 meter receiver, the signal-to-noise ratio is primarily determined by the noise that is generated where?

By the noise that's generated externally (man-made) and is picked up by the antenna system along with the signal itself.

167 Know the frequencies that an Advanced Class operator may use. See the chart following these questions.

168 An amateur radio station in repeater operation may legally be operated by remote control under what circumstances?

When devices have been installed and procedures have been implemented to insure compliance with the F.C.C. Rules and Regulations.

169 An amateur radio operator has adjusted the "netting" capacitor of his/her (I hate women's lib *only* because I have to keep doing this sort of nonsense!) 2 meter transmitter until a digital frequency counter connected to the output reads exactly 146,520,000 Hertz. If the frequency counter has a time base accuracy of plus or minus one (1) part per million (ppm), the actual transmitter frequency could differ from the reading of the frequency counter by how much?

Don't you just absolutely love the way that this question is so muddled up? Well, this is very close to the way it is reported to be worded on the actual F.C.C. exam. The solution is found by taking the number of millions that the frequency counter is reading (146.52) and then you multiply the number of millions by the amount of the time base accuracy, which in this case is simply multiplying by one and therefore we get 146.52 × 1 = 146.52 Hertz/Hz. When they say there is a time base accuracy of ±10 parts per million, then you'd multiply by 10 to get 146.52 × 10 = 1465.20 Hertz/Hz. See how to solve this sort of stuff? This has some application in reality and you should put this info in your file of notes in case you ever need it again.

170 What does "capture effect" mean?

Per page 463 of Shrader's, during FM, if a two signals exist and one is stronger than another, then the stronger of the two signals will end up "capturing" the oscillator frequency that is in the discriminator circuit. When this happens, the weaker of the two signals will not be heard. That's fine unless you are trying to work the weaker of the two stations, right? The non-captured signal does not produce any rf and therefore will not be heard. Please send the exact wording on this. Thanks!

171 What is "backwave radiation" and what causes it?

This is spelled out on page 350 of Shrader's as it applies to a master oscillator power amplifier (MOPA), which is a 2 stage transmitter. It is simply any signal from the oscillator that is leaking through.

Since this is undesirable, it may be prevented by properly neutralizing the amplifier, making sure that the power supply is adequately filtered, and not overdriving the final.

172 What's the most efficient amplifier of the following choices?

> a. Class A
> b. Class B
> c. Class C
> d. Class AB

The answer is Class C because it has an efficiency of about 60 percent (see page 323 of Shrader's). All other classes are lower in efficiency but produce "cleaner" output.

173 A grid dip meter can be used for what?

This is another variation of an earlier question, so be ready for it. They want you to know that you can use it to determine the frequency of a resonant circuit. Please see page 523 of ELECTRONIC COMMUNICATION by Robert L. Shrader for the details.

174 The response curve shown below is typical of what kind of filter?

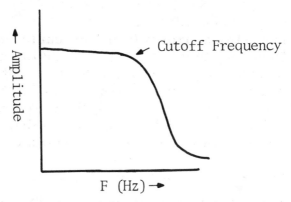

This is a simple low pass filter that is called a CONSTANT-K FILTER. As was pointed out elsewhere in the manual, a low pass filter will pass all of the received frequencies up to the value of its cutoff frequency and will block frequencies above the cutoff frequency. See page 137–138 of Shrader's for more details.

175 What happens to the impedance of a parallel RLC circuit if the frequency is increased?

In a parallel RLC circuit, impedance (z) is found by this formula:

$$Z = \frac{1}{\sqrt{\left(\frac{1}{R}\right)^2 + \left(\frac{1}{X_L} - \frac{1}{X_C}\right)^2}}$$

You'll recall that $X_L = 2\pi fL$ and $X_C = \frac{1}{2\pi fC}$. If you increase the frequency X_L will increase and X_C will decrease and the difference between X_L and X_C will increase. The net effect of all of this is that *an increase in frequency will result in a direct increase in impedance*. Please see pages 115 through 117 of Shrader's for details on these parallel circuits.

176 Briefly describe the operation of a silicon controlled rectifier (SCR).

Shown below is a schematic of an SCR.

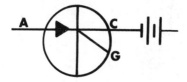

The current basically flows from the cathode (C) to the anode (A) through the device. Within the unit is a switch-like device called a gate (G). If the gate is closed, current can flow between the cathode and the anode. Once current has begun to flow, it will continue to flow regardless of the gate's status (meaning whether or not it's open or closed) until the supply source voltage (here we show a battery) is reduced to almost zero. Thus, an activated SCR is sometimes considered to behave like a piece of copper wire. Please see pages 188 and 189 of Shrader's for the details.

U.S. AMATEUR ADVANCED CLASS FREQUENCIES FOR HF/VHF BANDS

Frequencies in MEGAHERTZ

	CW	VOICE	RTTY-F1	TV
160 METERS	1.800 to 2.000	1.800–2.000	Prohibited	Prohibited
80 METERS	3.525 to 3.775	3.800 to 4.000	3.525 to 3.775	3.800 to 3.890
40 METERS	7.025 to 7.300	7.150 to 7.300	7.025 to 7.150	7.150 to 7.225
20 METERS	14.025 to 14.350	14.200 to 14.350	14.025 to 14.200	14.200 to 14.275
15 METERS	21.025 to 21.250	21.270 to 21.450	21.025 to 21.250	21.270 to 21.350
10 METERS	28.000 to 29.700	28.500 to 29.700	28.000 to 28.500	28.500 to 29.700
6 METERS	50.000 to 54.000	50.100 to 54.000	50.100 to 54.000	50.100 to 54.000
2 METERS	144.000 to 148.000	144.100 to 148.000	144.100 to 148.000	144.100 to 148.000

Repeater Operation

Above 29.5 MHz can use all frequencies EXCEPT:

    50.0–52.0 MHz   220.0–220.5 MHz
   144.0–144.5 MHz   431.0–433.0 MHz
   145.5–146.0 MHz   435.0–438.0 MHz

Auxiliary Operation

Above 220.5 can use all frequencies EXCEPT:

   431.0–433.0 MHz
   435.0–438.0 MHz

Scoreboard to Success

To gain the maximum benefit from this manual, please read from the front to here. Then place a check mark in box #10. Go back to the front of the manual and go through it again. When you get back to this page, please place a check mark in box #9. You've now done 2 passes and only need to make 8 more!

Continue in this manner until all the boxes are checked and then go take the F.C.C. exam. Do the 10 passes within a period of not more than 2 weeks. Smarter people than you and I (they're psychologists who specialize in learning) figured this crazy method out and it works!

10	9	8	7	6	5	4	3	2	1
☐	☐	☐	☐	☐	☐	☐	☐	☐	☐

In the Beginning...

Halfway Home!

One more time!

Bingo!

REVISION POLICY

Occasionally we have a sufficient number of changes and/or new questions to warrant the issuance of a revision for the manual. This material is available to you by sending us a 6″ × 9″ self addressed stamped envelope with 28¢ in stamps on it and the name of the revision (General, Advanced, Extra) written in the lower left hand corner of the S.A.S.E. Include $2.00 to cover duplication costs.

However, how do you know if there is a revision available before you go trotting off to the F.C.C. exam room? You simply telephone us and ask our office manager (her name is Sharon-KQ6A and she's pretty sharp; she's licensed as an Extra and knows her stuff) if we have one ready for you. If we do then send us the revision request, the SASE, the two bucks, etc. Then we'll shoot it right back to you. Nothing hard to understand about that, is there?

BOOKLIST

Shown below is a book list that you should have in your library at home. Of course, this is just my opinion but what the heck, you have to start some place! I have selected those books that are very readable and also have something in them that you *need* to know. Please purchase these manuals as you develop the finances to do so and *read* them. Let's face it: there is *no* substitute for knowledge! So, study the material in this manual carefully but, for Pete's sake, have an understanding of what this is all about!

1. **Electronic Communication by Robert L. Shrader— W6BNB (4th edition—published by McGraw-Hill). This is the best book around and costs $21.95.**

2. **Radio Handbook by William (Bill) I. Orr—W6SAI (21st edition—published by Howard W. Sams & Co.). A very comprehensive text and should be used!**

3. **Electronic Circuits for Technicians by Lloyd Temes (2nd edition—published by McGraw-Hill 1977). This book explains in terms most of us can understand how to solve circuit problems.**

4. **Communication Electronics for Technicians by Lloyd Temes (published by McGraw-Hill 1974). This manual works very well with Shrader's book to explain 90% of the questions showing up on exams. I like the way Temes explains things and so will you!**

5. **Practical Antennas for the Radio Amateur by Scelbi. (1st edition—published by Scelbi Publications). When used with the ARRL Antenna Book you get a great combination.**

6. **Electronics for the Amateur by Louis M. Dezettel— W5REZ (1st edition—published by Howard W. Sams & Co.). Provides a simple and not too detailed explanation of many problems we encounter.**

7. **Amateur Radio Theory Course by Martin Schwartz (1980 printing—published by AMECO Publishing Corp.). This is the classic old "grey AMECO book." Covers basics in readable detail.**

Mathematical Relationships

5. Resonant frequency, bandwidth, and "Q" of R-L-C circuits, given component values
6. Phase angle between voltage and current, given resistance and reactance
7. Power factor, given phase angle
8. Effective radiated power, given system gains and losses
9. Replacement of voltage source and resistive voltage divider with equivalent circuit consisting of a voltage source and one resistor (an application of thevenin's theorem, used to predict the current supplied by a voltage divider to a known load)

F. CIRCUIT COMPONENTS

Physical Appearance, Types, Characteristics, Applications, and Schematic Symbols for the Following:

1. Diodes; zener, tunnel, varactor, hot-carrier, junction, point contact, PIN
2. Transistors; npn, pnp, junction, unijunction, power, germanium, silicon
3. Silicon controlled rectifier, triac
4. Light emitting diode, neon lamp
5. Crystal lattice SSB filters

G. PRACTICAL CIRCUITS

1. Voltage regulator circuits; discrete and integrated
2. Amplifiers: class A, AB, B, C; characteristics of each type
3. Impedance matching networks; PI, L, PI-L
4. Filters; constant K, M-derived, band-stop, notch, modern-network-theory, PI-section, T-section, L-section (not necessary to memorize design equations; know description, characteristics, responses, and applications of these filters)
5. Oscillators; various types and their applications; stability

Transmitter and Receiver Circuits - Know Purpose of Each and How, Basically Each Functions:

6. Modulators; AM, FM, balanced
7. Transmitter final amplifiers
8. Detectors, mixer stages
9. RF and IF amplifier stages

Calculation of Voltages, Currents, and Power In Common Amateur Radio Oriented Circuits:

10. Common emitter class A transistor amplifier; bias network, signal gain, input and output impedances
11. Common collector class A transistor amplifier; bias network, signal gain, input and output impedances

Circuit Design; Selection of Circuit Component Values:

12. Voltage regulator with pass transistor and zener diode to produce given output voltage
13. Select coil and capacitor to resonate at given frequency

H. SIGNALS AND EMISSIONS

    1. Emission types A4, A5, F4, F5
    2. Modulation methods
    3. Deviation ratio
    4. Modulation index
    5. Electromagnetic radiation
    6. Wave polarization
    7. Sine, square, sawtooth waveforms
    8. Root mean square value
    9. Peak envelope power relative to average
   10. Signal to noise ratio

I. ANTENNAS AND FEEDLINES

    1. Antenna gain, beamwidth
    2. Trap antennas
    3. Parasitic elements
    4. Radiation resistance
    5. Driven elements
    6. Efficiency of antenna
    7. Folded, multiple wire dipoles
    8. Velocity factor
    9. Electrical length of a feedline
   10. Voltage and current nodes
   11. Mobile antennas
   12. Loading coil; base, center, top

STUDY TOPICS FOR THE AMATEUR EXTRA CLASS AMATEUR RADIO OPERATOR LICENSE EXAMINATION

A. RULES AND REGULATIONS

1. Frequency bands available to the U.S. amateur radio operator and limitations on their use including variations for regions 1 & 3 97.61; 97.95
2. Space amateur radio stations 97.3 (i)
3. Purity of emissions 97.73
4. Mobile operation aboard ships or aircraft 97.101
5. Races operation Part 97, Subpart F
6. Points of communications 97.89

B. OPERATING PROCEDURES

1. Use of amateur radio satellites
2. Amateur fast scan television

C. RADIO WAVE PROPAGATION

1. EME; "moonbounce"
2. Meteor burst
3. Trans-equatorial

D. AMATEUR RADIO PRACTICE

Use of Test Equipment:
1. Spectrum analyzer; interpret display; display of transmitter output spectrum, such as commonly found in new product review articles in amateur radio magazines
2. Logic probe; indication of high or low state, pulsing state

Electromagnetic Compatability:
3. Vehicle noise suppression; ignition noise, alternator whine, static
4. Direction finding techniques; methods for location of source of radio signals

E. ELECTRICAL PRINCIPLES

Concepts:
1. Photoconductive effect
2. Exponential charge/discharge

Mathematical Relationships; Calculations:
3. Time constant for R-C and R-L circuits (including circuits with more than one resistor, capacitor, or inductor)
4. Impedance diagrams; basic principles of Smith chart
5. Impedance of R-L-C networks at a specified frequency
6. Algebraic operations using complex numbers; real, imaginary, magnitude, angle

F. CIRCUIT COMPONENTS

Physical Appearance, Types, Characteristics, Applications, and Schematic Symbols for:
1. Field effect transistors; enhancement, depletion, MOS, CMOS, n-channel, p-channel
2. Operational amplifier and phase-locked loop integrated circuits
3. 7400 series TTL digital integrated circuits
4. 4000 series cmos digital integrated circuits
5. Vidicon; cathode ray tube

G. PRACTICAL CIRCUITS

1. Digital logic circuits; flip-flop, multivibrator, and/or/nand/nor/gates
3. ACtive audio filters using integrated operational amplifiers

High Performance Reciever Characteristics
4. Noise figure, sensitivity
5. Selectivity
6. Dynamic range

Calculation of Voltages, Currents, and Power In Common Amateur Radio Oriented Circuits:
7. Integrated operational amplifier; voltage gain, frequency response
8. F.E.T. common source amplifier; input impedance

Circuit Design; Selection of Circuit Component Values:
9. L-C preselector with fixed and variable capacitors to tune a given frequency range
10. Single stage amplifier to have desired frequency response by proper selection of bypass and coupling capacitors

H. SIGNALS AND EMISSIONS

1. Pulse modulation; position, width
2. Digital signals
3. Narrow band voice modulation
4. Information rate vs. bandwidth
5. Peak amplitude of signal
6. Peak-to-peak values of a signal

I. ANTENNAS AND FEEDLINES

1. Antennas for space radio communications; gain, beamwidth, tracking
2. Isotropic radiator; use as a standard of comparison
3. Phased vertical antennas; resultant patterns, spacing in wavelengths
4. Rhombic antennas; advantages, disadvantages
5. Matching antenna to feedline; delta, gamma, stub
6. Properties of 1/8, 1/4, 3/8 and 1/2 wavelength sections of feedlines; shorted, open

Home Remedies for TV Interference

HOME REMEDIES FOR RESOLVING RADIO TRANSMITTER INTERFERENCE

Installing A High-Pass Filter

There are no set procedures for eliminating television interference—it is a matter of eliminating the most likely sources of interference a step at a time. The first step is to install an inexpensive high-pass filter on the back of your TV set. In making this installation, follow these procedures:

1. Determine the type of antenna wire that is connected to your TV set. There are two possibilities:

Coaxial Cable—a round lead-in wire which requires a filter "impedance" of 75 ohms. (See Figure 1a.)

Twin Lead Wire—a flat wire which requires a filter "impedance" of 300 ohms. (See Figure 1b.)

2. Purchase the filter which matches the type of antenna wire coming from your set. The "impedance" information mentioned above will be on the filter label. DO NOT use a combination of twin-lead and coaxial cable without proper matching transformers (often called baluns). Filters are available in most stores that sell or repair television sets. Figure 2 provides a small example of what high-pass filters look like.

3. Carefully read the instructions that are provided with the filter. You will be installing the filter on the back of your TV set, as near to the antenna terminal as possible. The antenna terminal and the filter terminal will look like either Figure 1a or 1b depending upon the type of wire you are using—coaxial or twin lead.

4. If you are on a cable system, you may still install the filter at the antenna terminal. However, if the interference continues, contact the cable company repair service for assistance. DO NOT attempt to modify the cable system yourself.

5. The following information on installing the filter should answer any additional questions you may have.

a. Disconnect the antenna wire (twin-lead or coaxial) from the television set antenna terminals.

b. Connect the wire from the antenna to the input terminals of the filter.

c. For twin-lead wire, connect a very short (1" to 2") "jumper" wire from the antenna input terminals of the set to the filter (see Figure 3). For coaxial cable, it will be necessary to obtain a jumper cable that has the proper connectors already installed. (This can be purchased at the time you buy the coaxial filter.)

d. Be sure that in the case of **TWIN-LEAD WIRE**, the actual wires are making

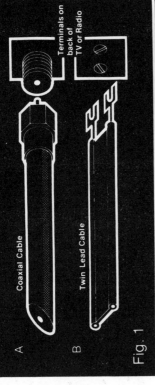

A Coaxial Cable

B Twin Lead Cable

Terminals on back of TV or Radio

Fig. 1

Fig. 2

Montage of Filters

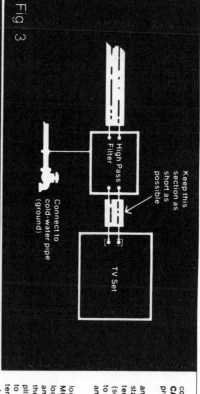

Fig. 3

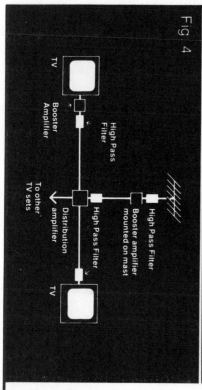

Fig. 4

contact with the terminals. For **COAXIAL CABLE**, be sure the connector plugs are properly installed on the coaxial cable.

e. If you have an amplifier in your antenna system, you should have a filter installed ahead of the amplifier and another filter ahead of the TV receiver input terminals (see Figure 4). If the amplifier is located close to the receiver, then install the filter before the amplifier only.

Note: BOOSTER amplifiers usually are located near the back of the TV set; MAST MOUNTED (Outdoor) amplifiers are usually located on the antenna; and DISTRIBUTION amplifiers are usually located somewhere in the distribution system. If a distribution amplifier is in your antenna system, then be sure to trace the entire length of the antenna system, because amplifiers are usually in out-of-the-way places (for example—clothes closets, basements, etc.)

f. The connecting wires between the filter and amplifier, and between the amplifier and antenna terminal, should be as short as possible.

g. The instructions provided with the filter you bought may call for a ground connection. The wire should be as short as possible and connected between the high-pass filter ground terminal and a metallic cold water pipe or a ground rod. Use bell wire for this connection (see Figure 3). Bell wire can be obtained from most variety stores.

h. If installation of the filter at the TV antenna terminals does not entirely eliminate the interference, you should then contact your service representative to install a high-pass filter inside the TV set at the tuner input terminals. INTERNAL modifications to your set should be done ONLY by a service representative. Information to assist your service representative is contained in the Technical Information for Service Representatives section.

Home Remedies for Resolving Electrical Interference

Electrical interference is caused by two sources:
1. Vehicle ignition systems.
2. Electrical devices.
The first step in attempting to resolve electrical interference problems is to locate the source of interference.

Interference from Vehicle Ignition System

1. Ignition interference sounds like a "popping" noise in the sound system of your TV that rises in intensity; the "pops" occur closer and closer together as the speed of the engine speeds up. This can be caused by any vehicle ignition system, such as gasoline operated lawn mowers, snowmobiles, automobiles, etc.
2. If the interference is to television receivers, you may hear the same popping noise in the sound and also see "dancing dots" in the picture of the set. You may only see the interference, and not hear the "popping" noise in the sound.
3. If your own vehicle is causing interference, you may wish to install a commercially manufactured kit in your vehicle to reduce the ignition noise. Other remedial measures include relocating your antenna, raising the antenna, and using shielded lead-in antenna wire.

Interference from Electrical Devices

1. Any one or more of the following electrical devices may be causing the interference you are experiencing on your television set or AM/FM radio:
Electric razor, Vacuum cleaner, Fan, Drill, Electric blankets, Bake ovens, Fluorescent lights, Arc lights, Light dimmer controls, Relays, Static from machinery, Lightning arrestors, Adding machine, Cash register, Circuit beakers, Ultra-violet lamps, Germicidal lamps, Defective wiring, Loose fuse, Arc welder, Switch contacts (such as on dishwashers and other home appliances), Refrigerator, Water pump, Sewing machine, Light blinkers (including Christmas tree light blinker), Electric heating pads, Aquarium warmers, Neon signs, Door bell circuits/transformers, Toys (such as electric trains), Sign flashers, Antifriction bearings, Printing press static eliminators, Calculator, Insulators, Incandescent lamp (new or old), Sun lamps, Electrical pole (ground wire cut or poor contact), Loose electrical connection, Electric fence unit, Furnace controls, Power company transformers, Smoke precipitators.

2. In attempting to locate the specific device causing the interference, consider the following suggestions:
a. If you have a portable radio that is affected by the interference, use the radio as a detection device to assist in locating the source of interference. With the portable radio, move from room to room and determine in which room the interference appears to be the loudest. Then look for one of the devices listed above and unplug it to see if the interference disappears. If several devices listed above are in the room, unplug them, one at a time, until the interference disappears.
b. If a portable radio is not affected, you can go to the main fuse or circuit breaker box in your home, remove one fuse at a time, or shut off one breaker at a time, and see if the interference goes away.
c. If it does not go away when the first fuse or circuit breaker is off, replace the fuse or turn the circuit breaker back on and continue on until the interference does disappear. When the circuit that supplies the power to the TV or radio is turned off, it will be necessary to plug that device into some other circuit to determine if the interference is being generated by a device in the same room as your TV or radio.
d. When the interference disappears with a fuse removed or circuit breaker off, you should go to the room supplied by that circuit and look for any of the devices listed above. If any of the listed devices are found in the room, replace the fuse or turn the circuit breaker back on. Then unplug the device suspected of causing the interference. If several devices are in the room, unplug them, one at a time.

3. If you are unable to locate within your own home the device that is causing the problem, the interference may be coming from a device located in your neighbor's home. With the cooperation of your neighbor, follow the same procedures described above.

4. If your investigation leads you to suspect that a power line or power company equipment is the source of interference, you should contact the power company to assist you in resolving the problem.

5. Short duration interference, such as that from electric drills and saws, may be very costly to attempt to eliminate; you may just want to "live with it."

6. To resolve electrical interference, modifications must be made to the interfering device. This should only be done by a qualified service representative. Information for your service representative is contained in the Technical Information for Service Representatives section.

Home Remedies for Resolving FM Interference

The installation of an inexpensive FM band rejection filter is the first step to take in resolving FM interference. In making this installation, follow these procedures:

1. Determine the type of antenna wire you have connected to your TV set. There are two possibilities:

Coaxial Cable—a round lead-in wire which requires a filter "impedance" of 75 ohms (see Figure 1a).

Twin Lead Wire—a flat wire which requires a filter "impedance" of 300 ohms (see Figure 1b).

2. Purchase the appropriate filter, according to the type of antenna wire you have. The "impedance" information mentioned above will be on the filter label. DO NOT use a combination of twin-lead and coaxial cable without proper matching transformers (often called baluns). Filters are available in most stores that sell or repair television sets.

3. Carefully read the instructions that are provided with the filter. You will be installing the filter on the back of your TV set, as near to the antenna terminal as possible. The antenna terminal and the filter terminal will look like either Figure 1a or 1b depending upon the type of wire you are using—coaxial cable or twin-lead wire.

4. If you are on a cable system, you may still install the same FM band rejection filter at the antenna terminal. However, if the interference continues, contact the cable company repair service for assistance. DO NOT attempt to modify the cable system yourself.

5. The following information on installing the filter should answer any additional questions you may have.

a. Disconnect the antenna wire antenna terminals.

b. Connect the wire from the antenna to the input terminals of the filter.

c. For twin-lead wire, connect a very short (1" to 2") "jumper" wire from the antenna input terminals of the set to the filter (see Figure 3). For coaxial cable, it will be necessary to obtain a jumper cable that has the proper connectors already installed.

d. Be sure that in the case of TWIN LEAD WIRE, the actual wires are making contact with the terminals. For COAXIAL CABLE, be sure the connector plugs are properly installed on the coaxial cable.

e. If you have an amplifier in your antenna system, you should have a filter installed before the amplifier and another filter ahead of the TV receiver input terminals (see Figure 4). If the amplifier is located close to the receiver, then install the filter before the amplifier only.

Note: BOOSTER amplifiers usually are located near the back of the TV set; MAST MOUNTED (outdoor) amplifiers are usually located on the antenna; and DISTRIBUTION amplifiers are usually located somewhere in the distribution system. If a distribution amplifier is in your antenna system, then be sure to trace the entire length of the antenna system, because amplifiers are usually in out-of-the-way places (for example—clothes closets, basements, etc.)

f. The connecting wires between the filter and amplifier, and between the amplifier and antenna terminal, should be as short as possible

g. The instructions provided with the filter you bought may call for a ground connection. The wire should be as short as possible and connected between the FM band rejection filter ground terminal and a metallic cold water pipe or a ground rod. Use bell wire for this connection (see Figure 3). Bell wire can be obtained from most variety stores.

h. If the filter does not entirely eliminate the interference, you should call your service representative. The Technical Information for Service Representatives Section is provided to assist the service representative.

Audio Interference

Identification of Audio Interference

Interference to audio devices, such as tape recorders, record players, electronic organs, telephones, hi-fi amplifiers, etc., is caused when the equipment responds to the transmission of a nearby radio transmitter.

Audio interference (often called audio rectification) may also affect the sound (audio) portion of your TV and AM/FM radio.

When this type of interference is occurring, you will hear the voice transmissions of the radio transmitter and/or the volume level of the audio device you are using may decrease.

If you have determined that this is the type of interference you are receiving, refer to the following Home Remedies section for suggested methods for eliminating audio interference.

Home Remedies for Resolving Audio Interference

Audio interference is a condition that usually requires internal modification of your equipment. For safety reasons, it is recommended that any modifications be made by a qualified service representative.

Due to the complexity of resolving interference to an electronic organ, again, servicing should be done only by an experienced service representative. More detailed information should be obtained from the equipment manufacturer.

For telephone interference, contact your local telephone company. They can install a 1542A or similar inductor in the telephone instrument to resolve the problem. The information provided in this bulletin applies primarily to privately-owned equipment and should not be applied to equipment owned by the telephone company. Bell System personnel can obatin additional data in Section 500-150-100 of the "Bell System Practices—Plant Series" manual.

For all other audio devices, you may wish to take the following steps before calling your service representative.

1. Replace UNSHIELDED wire between the amplifier and speakers with SHIELDED wire.

2. Ground the affected equipment to a metallic cold water pipe or ground rod. A ground connection can be made with a short piece of "bell wire" which can be obtained at most variety stores. DO NOT ground "AC-DC" type devices. Normally devices which may safely be grounded will provide a grounding terminal. If no terminal is provided, then you should consult a qualified service representative for advice.

3. If the interference is not eliminated after taking these steps you must call a qualified service representative. The Technical Information for Service Representatives section is provided to assist your service representative in resolving the problem. You may also wish to discuss the matter with the operator of the radio transmitter, sharing the information in the Radio Operator Guidelines section of this bulletin.

79

Technical Information

Technical Information for Service Representatives

Resolving Radio Transmitter Interference

There are no set procedures for eliminating television interference—it is a matter of eliminating the most likely sources of interference a step at a time. You may be required to take several steps before the interference problem is resolved. Once you have installed the filter called for, or made the adjustment that you were instructed to do, leave the modifications in place and proceed to the next step.

To begin, check to see if a high-pass filter has been installed on the TV set at the antenna terminals. If not, read the Home Remedy information beginning on page 5. If the interference is still present after the installation of a high-pass filter proceed with the following steps.

Check Radio Transmitter

1. Contact the operator of the radio transmitter identified as the source and, with his/her cooperation, determine if the transmitter is operating properly. You may also wish to share the Radio Operator Guidelines section of this bulletin with the operator. Areas of concern should be:

a. Is the transmitter properly grounded? (This means a good radio frequency (**RF**) ground. A single piece of wire to a ground rod may be an open circuit to **RF**.)

b. Are harmonics and/or spurious emissions present?

c. Is the transmitter cabinet radiating energy?

2. If the transmitter is not grounded, connect the chassis to a good earth ground

with large diameter wire or copper strap. This should assist in eliminating radiation of energy from the cabinet.

3. Next, install a low-pass filter on the transmitter antenna circuit to see if any difference occurs in the interference pattern. If a change occurs, the interference is probably caused by harmonics and/or spurious emissions from the transmitter. If no change occurs in the interference pattern, it is probably being generated at some point in the TV reception system.

Check TV Reception System

1. Conduct a visual inspection of the TV antenna, lead-in wire, and lightning arrestors. This may reveal a source of trouble. Corroded connections or deteriorated lead-in wire could be at fault and should be repaired.

2. Assuming no faulty conditions are found, or if found, they are corrected, and the interference is still present, look for an amplifier in the line. Amplifiers are highly susceptible to radio frequency (**RF**) energy.

Note: BOOSTER amplifiers usually are located near the back of the TV set; MAST MOUNTED (outdoor) amplifiers are usually located on the antenna; and DISTRIBUTION amplifiers are usually located somewhere in the distribution system. If a distribution amplifier is in the antenna system, then be sure to trace the entire length of the antenna system, because amplifiers are usually in out-of-the-way places (for example—clothes closets, basements, etc.).

3. If an amplifier is in the system, remove it from the circuit. If you find that this eliminates the interference, reconnect the amplifier, but protect the amplifier by a) grounding,

b) enclosing it in a metallic rf-proof housing and grounding the housing, or c) installing a high-pass filter at the input to the amplifier. If one filter improves the condition, but does not entirely eliminate the interference, install two filters in series.

4. If no amplifier is utilized, or the interference still persists after following one or all of the above steps, check the TV receiver system.

Check TV Receiver System

1. An AC power line **RF** filter should be installed to determined if the **RF** from the transmitter is entering the TV via the power cord. (A line filter may be either purchased or one may be constructed by following the schematic in Figure 5.)

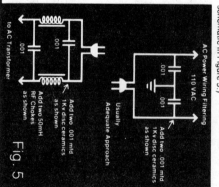

AC Power Wiring Filtering

110 VAC

Add two .001 mfd
1Kv disc ceramics
as shown

.001 .001

Usually
Adequate Approach

to AC Transformer

Add two .001 mfd
1Kv disc ceramics
as shown

Add two 50mH
RF Chokes
as shown

.001

.001

Fig. 5

1μh choke

2-20pf ceramic trimmer

Fig. 6

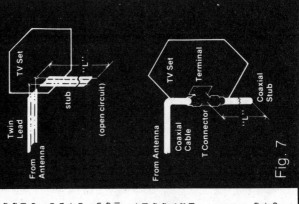

From Antenna

Twin Lead

TV Set

stub

"L"

(open circuit)

From Antenna

Coaxial Cable

T Connector

TV Set

Terminal

"L"

Coaxial Stub

Fig. 7

2. If no change is found with the power line filter installed, and the antenna disconnected, then the set itself is responding to the **RF** energy.

3. The most likely internal circuit in the set to be affected by a radio transmitter is the tuner. Disconnect the antenna input lead inside the set directly at the tuner. If the interference is eliminated, then install a high-pass filter at the tuner.

4. If the interference is still present after installing the filter at the tuner, it will be necessary to refer to service data for the set and check each stage of the set for undesired response.

CB Interference to TV Channel 2

1. Second harmonic interference from a CB transmitter to Channel 2 television may exist even though the transmitter meets FCC specifications for harmonic radiation. In such cases, a tuned filter across the antenna terminals of the television should help. The filter may be an inductor and capacitor in series as in Figure 6. The filter should be tuned for minimum interference.

2. A second method is to put an open circuit, quarter-wave, tuned stub across the antenna terminals. The stub should be made of the same type of wire as the antenna input terminals of the television. The initial stub length should be 37" for RG-59/U coax; and 48" for 300 ohm twin lead.

3. After connecting the stub, cut the unterminated end of the stub off in 1/8" to 1/4" sections until the interference is eliminated. Refer to Figure 7. For harmonics falling on other TV channels, such as channel 5, 6, or

9, the length of the stub may be appropriately shortened according to the following formula.

$$\text{Length in inches} = \frac{2952V}{f}$$

where **V** = Velocity factor of line
and **f** = frequency in megahertz

Amateur Interference to TV Channel 2

1. One additional type of interference from a nearby transmitter is unique to the amateur 6 meter band—50-54 MHz. Since 6 meters is immediately adjacent to Channel 2 television (54-60 MHz), interference to Channel 2 may occur.

2. In most cases, installation of an open circuit, quarterwave, tuned stub at the antenna terminals of the television set should be effective. It should be connected as shown in Figure 7.

3. If RG-59/U is used as the TV lead-in wire, the initial length of the stub should be 42". If 300 ohm twin lead is used, the initial length should be 53".

4. After the stub is attached to the television, begin cutting off the unterminated end of the stub 1/8" to 1/4" at a time until the interference is eliminated. If the interference is reduced, but not eliminated by this method, add a second stub directly to the input terminals of the tuner. The theoretical final length of the stub should be:

$$\text{Length in inches} = \frac{2952V}{f}$$

Where **V** = Velocity factor of line
and **f** = frequency in megahertz

5. If the interference continues, share the information in the Radio Operator Guidelines section with the operator of the radio transmitter.

Resolving Electrical Interference

1. Please read through the procedures outlined in the Home Remedies section, beginning on page 7, before proceeding. If the steps in the previous section have been taken, you should now know the source of the interference.

2. Before proceeding with the following steps to modify the device located as the source of interference, you should check the local electrical codes to determine if the device may be modified, and whether a licensed electrician must modify the device.

Caution: All bypassing of devices with capacitors should be done with extreme care to insure that the capacitors do not short out the AC line. Dangerous voltages exist which can cause electrocution if mishandled. Also, avoid power wiring which can cause the full AC line voltage to appear on the case of the device.

3. Since interference from an electric drill or saw may be of short duration, we suggest no modifications be made to the device. Mainly because it may be very difficult and time-consuming to modify the device. If, however, interference is of long duration, and you wish to take on this task, proceed as follows:

   a. Interference from a drill or saw is actually caused by arcing between the brushes and commutator. The interference then is transmitted through the power cord. Bypassing each side of the line to ground with a capacitor, and each side to the other may be helpful. Also bypass the switch. Figure 8 shows the schematic involved. The bypassing should be internal to the device in question.

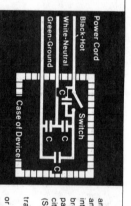

Power Cord
Black-Hot
White-Neutral
Green-Ground

Switch

Case of Device

Fig. 8 c = .001 mfd., disc ceramic

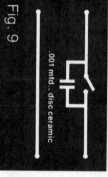

Fig. 9 c = .001 mfd. disc ceramic

Fig. 10

Black-Hot

Dimmer

C

White-Neutral

C

Light

.001 mfd., disc ceramic

4. Electric blankets, fish tank heaters, and other thermostatically controlled appliances, with worn and pitted contacts, cause interference because of contact arcing of the breaker points. This can be eliminated by bypassing the contacts with a .001 mfd capacitor or replacing the worn or pitted contacts. (See Figure 9.)

5. Defective devices such as doorbell transformers should be replaced.

6. Dimmer switches that utilize an SCR or triac can produce tremendous interference and it is very difficult to eliminate. This is due to the approximate square wave output that is produced by the switching at the SCR or triac. However, bypassing in a manner shown in Figure 10 may be helpful.

7. Since resolving electrical interference has to proceed on a case-by-case basis, you should always consider adequately bypassing any component of the circuit that arcs or distorts the AC sine wave with ceramic condensers.

Resolving FM Interference

There are no set procedures for eliminating FM interference—it is a matter of eliminating the most likely sources of interference a step at a time. You may be required to take several steps before the interference problem is resolved. Once you have installed the filter called for, or made the adjustment that you were instructed to do, leave the modifications in place and proceed to the next step.

1. To begin, check to see if an FM band rejection filter has been installed on the TV set at the antenna terminals. If not, read the Home Remedies section of this bulletin, beginning on page 8.

2. If the installation of an FM band rejection filter is not effective, then a tuned stub

trap should be constructed (see example in Figure 11). The trap should be placed on and parallel to the lead-in and tuned for minimum interference. Then slide the trap along the line to further reduce interference. Finally, tape the trap to the lead-in in the most effective position.

3. Another type of stub, called an open circuit quarter-wave type, can be made from the same type of wire as the antenna lead-in wire (see Figure 12). The initial length of the stub should be 24" for RG-59/U coaxial cable or 29" for 300 ohm twin-lead wire. For other cables, the initial length can be determined by the general formula:

Length in inches = (35) (Velocity factor of line)

Note: If "F" type tee connectors are not available, you may use BNC type connectors.

4. If connecting the stub to the antenna terminals is not completely effective, connect a second stub of the same length directly to the input terminals of the tuner, inside the television set. This should eliminate the interference.

Resolving Audio Interference

1. Audio interference is defined as reception of radio frequency (**RF**) energy by an audio amplifier. The **RF** energy is then rectified, or more properly "detected", by an electron tube, transistor, diode, poor solder joint or ground, or integrated circuit. The detected signal is then treated identically as a normal audio signal appearing at the amplifier input terminals. The effects of audio interference vary with the type of modulation employed by the transmitter. The following chart shows expected effects:

AM—The voice or music will be heard as any normal audio signal applied to the amplifier. The voice or music may be extremely loud and slightly distorted.

SSB—Single Sideband—The voice will sound practically unintelligible and garbled.

FM—Usually no sound will be heard; however, a decrease in the volume of the amplifier will be noted when the radio transmitter is on. Clicks may be heard when a two-way radio transmitter is keyed and unkeyed. A "frying" noise (such as bacon sizzling) may also be heard.

TV—Audio rectification of a TV signal will sound like a buzz. The buzz will change its sound as the television picture changes.

2. In attempting to isolate where in the audio chain the rectification is taking place, check to determine if the volume control has any effect on the interference. If the volume of the interfering signal changes with a change in the volume control, then the rectification is occurring BEFORE the volume control. If the volume control has minimal or no effect, the rectification is occurring AFTER the volume control. You should next proceed to the appropriate set of solutions. If the solutions described below do not resolve the audio interference problem, contact the manu-

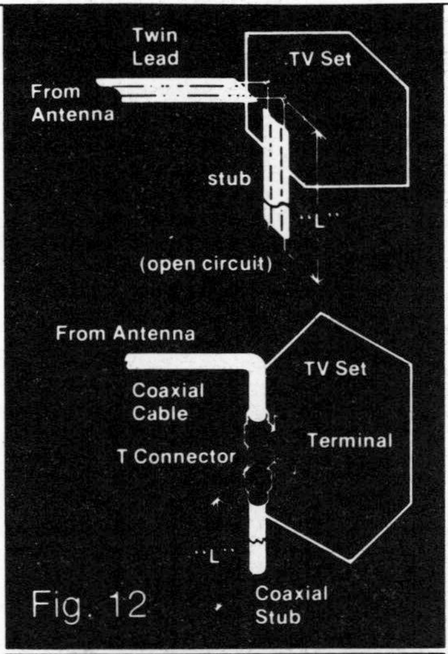

From Antenna
Twin Lead
TV Set
stub
(open circuit)

Fig. 12

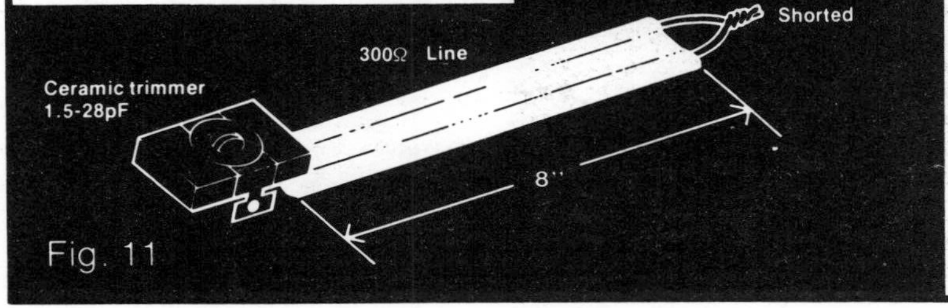

From Antenna
Coaxial Cable
T Connector
TV Set
Terminal
Coaxial Stub
"L"

Fig. 11

Ceramic trimmer
1.5-28pF
300Ω Line
8"
Shorted

facturer of the audio device for further assistance.

Rectification Before the Volume Control

1. A multiple input audio amplifier may be susceptible to audio interference on only one or some of the available inputs. Generally, low-level, high-impedance inputs, such as those in turn-tables, cartridges, tape heads, or microphones, are the most susceptible. If, for example, the only input affected is from a turn-table, then disconnect the turn-table cartridge from the amplifier at the input terminals of the amplifier.

2. If the interference is eliminated, then the cartridge, or wire between the cartridge and amplifier, is sensing the **RF**. Proper grounding, connections, shielding, and **RF** bypassing are the keys to solving audio rectification. Often, a "process of elimination" approach must be used.

Grounding

1. All grounding should be to a good earth ground such as a metallic cold water pipe or 8' ground rod. Ground leads should be as short as possible. Remember, a DC ground may appear as an open circuit to **RF** energy. Ground leads should be of as large a diameter wire as practicable. Finally, grounding of the chassis, shields of speaker leads, and other external connections should be made to a common point to avoid ground loops. (Ground loops are circuits that form a DC ground, but contain RF circulating currents.) Figure 15 shows the correct and incorrect methods of grounding components.

Caution: Some equipment chassis are at line voltage potential and cannot be con-

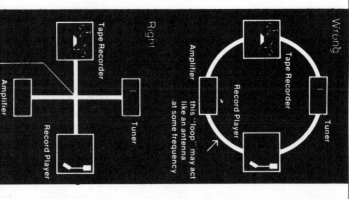

Fig. 13

nected directly to ground. In these circumstances, a ceramic capacitor of 0.001 mfd at 1Kv should be placed in the ground lead. This capacitor appears as a a short to **RF**, but an open circuit to AC.

Shielding

1. All speaker leads from audio equipment should be made of two conductor shielded wires. The shield should be grounded only at the amplifier end, and should not be used as an audio conductor. The two internal wires should be connected to the speaker.

Power Line Filter

1. **RF** may be entering the audio device through the AC power line. Several power line filters are commercially available. If necessary, a power line filter like the one shown in Figure 5 may be constructed, placing the filter as close as possible to the point where the AC cord enters the amplifier.

Poor Electrical Connections

1. Occasionally, poor solder connections or old electrolytic capacitors may be the cause of the audio rectification problem. If tests to this point have failed, try resoldering all connections in the amplifier and replacing electrolytic capacitors. Before actually replacing the electrolytic capacitor, try paralleling the capacitor with another one of like value. This should reveal the presence of a bad capacitor.

Rectification After the Volume Control

1. When the volume control is in its minimum position, and the interference is still heard, then an **RF** filter is required in the audio amplifier. It is extremely important that

R stop

Fig. 15

RF Choke

Fig. 14

Fig. 16

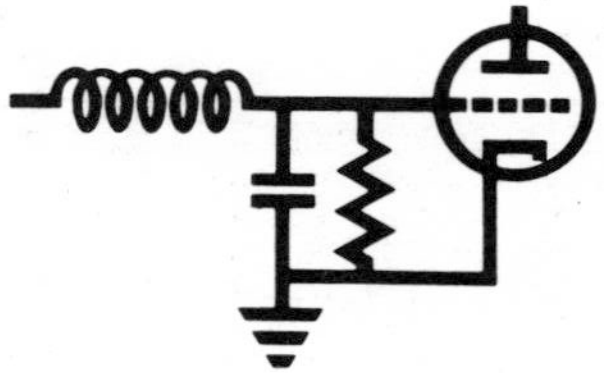

A combination RC filter is shown in Figure 17 with the recommended values.

the filter does not affect the audio response of the amplifier.

Tube Type Equipment

1. Interference in tube type equipment can be avoided by connecting an RF choke (ranging in value from 2 millihenry to 5 millihenry) in the upper end of the cathode circuit as shown in Figure 14.

2. The choke coil must NOT be bypassed by a capacitor because the DC resistance of such coil is generally quite low and the bias voltage is not greatly affected. However, if the DC resistance does affect the bias voltage, the value of the bias resistor may be decreased to compensate for the DC resistance of the choke.

3. A grid-stopping or "swamping" resistor can also be employed. A resistor, ranging in value from 1 k to 75 k ohms, can be connected in series with the grid as shown in Figure 15.

4. Capacitors, **RF** chokes and resistors can be used in combinations to make filters to eliminate the interference. For circuits such as those shown in Figure 16, use a choke of 2 to 6 microhenries and a capacitor of about 10 picofards. A combination RF filter is shown in Figure 17 with the recommended values.

Transistor Equipment

1. Interference in transistor equipment can usually be eliminated with the use of a shunt capacitor as shown in Figure 18. A resistor/capacitor combination can be used as shown in Figure 19. It is important that the filter network does not affect the biasing of the transistor or the frequency response of the amplifier.

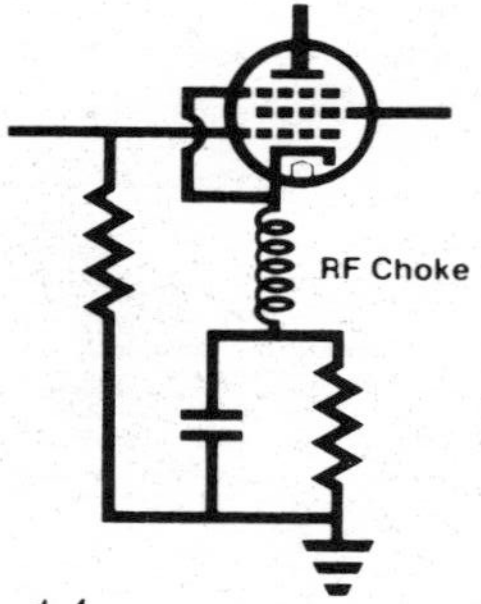

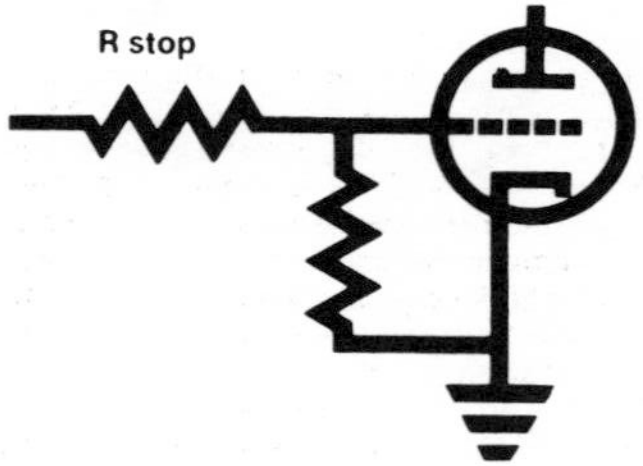

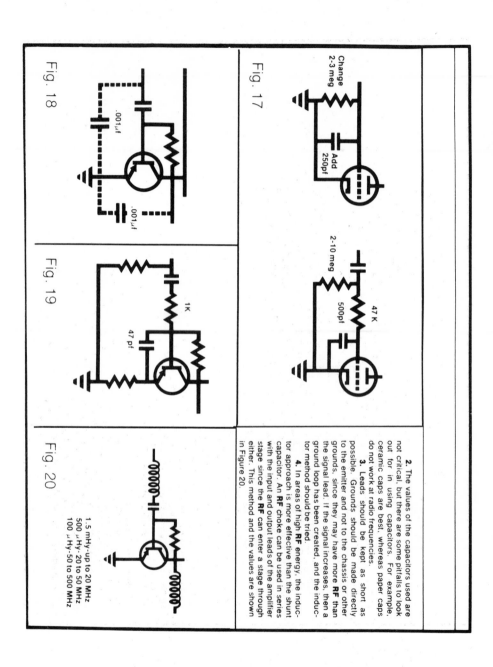

Fig. 17

Change
2-3 meg

Add
250pf

2-10 meg

500pf

47 K

Fig. 18

.001μf

.001μf

Fig. 19

1k

47 pf

Fig. 20

1.5 mHy-up to 20 MHz
500 μHy-20 to 50 MHz
100 μHy-50 to 500 MHz

2. The values of the capacitors used are not critical, but there are some pitfalls to look out for in using capacitors. For example, ceramic caps are best, whereas paper caps do not work at radio frequencies.

3. Leads should be kept as short as possible. Grounds should be made directly to the emitter and not to the chassis or other grounds, since they may have more **RF** than the signal lead. If the signal increases, then a ground loop has been created, and the inductor method should be tried.

4. In areas of high **RF** energy, the inductor approach is more effective than the shunt capacitor. An **RF** choke can be used in series with the input and output leads of the amplifier stage since the **RF** can enter a stage through either. This method and the values are shown in Figure 20.

Electronic Organs

1. Organ circuits can be isolated by the use of the Swell Pedal, band box volume, or tabs (draw bars). By adjusting each one of these different controls, the effect on the interference can be noted. If the volume of the interference changes, the RF is being detected by the amplifier at a point before that particular control. If the volume of the interference does not change, then the interference is being detected after that control.

2. Using this method, the point at which the RF is entering the organ can be determined, and the appropriate filter, as described above, can be inserted into the circuit.

Telephones

1. Telephone **RF** interference can be eliminated by the use of a 1542A or similar inductor. This inductor must be installed inside the phone and not at the baseboard. To install the inductor inside the phone, the corners of the plastic container will have to be removed. If the phone is too small for the inductor, such as the "Princess" telephone, then a pair of 2.5 MH chokes (75 ma or higher) must be installed inside the phone, one on each side of the line and as close to the 211A equalizing network as possible.

Note: The information provided here applies primarily to privately owned equipment and should not be applied to equipment owned by the telephone company. Telephone company owned equipment should be modified only by telephone company personnel. Bell System personnel can obtain additional data in Section 500-150-100 of the "Bell System Practices—Plant Series" manual.

References

1. *The Audio Cyclopedia* by Howard M. Tremline, Howard W. Sams and Co., Inc.

2. *Radio Handbook* by William I. Orr, Editors and Engineers, Ltd.

3. *The Radio Amateur's Handbook* by American Radio Relay League.

4. *Thomas Tech-Flash*, Thomas Organ Co., Sepulveda, California.

5. "Filtering RF Interference in Audio Equipment", by R. S. MacCollister from Journal of the Audio Engineering Society, April 1968, Pages 210, 212, 214.

6. *Stopping Telephone Interference* by Irvin M. Hoff, QST, March 1968, Pages 46-47.

Radio Transmitter Operator Guidelines

Resolution of Interference for Radio Transmitter Operators

Although some interference problems can be attributed to television receivers, such problems can also be traced to CB radio transmitters. Therefore, upon receipt of an interference complaint from your neighbor(s), you should take all steps possible to insure that your radio transmitter is not causing the interference. Voluntary installation of a low-pass filter, or other steps as outlined below, may eliminate the interference, and may prevent you from receiving an order from the Commission to implement these measures. You are not, however, required to service or add filtering to the complainant's television, and should not take any such action without the full cooperation of your neighbors.

You are cautioned that the use of an amateur transceiver on the Citizens Band is illegal. Further, the use of external **RF** power amplifiers with CB transceivers is illegal. Both actions may subject you to Commission actions or criminal penalties.

Generally, transmitter equipment that is commercially manufactured and type-accepted by the Commission has precautions built into the set to reduce harmonic radiation. Harmonics are radiations that are multiples of the operating frequency. However, you should follow the steps outlined below to insure that your radio equipment is operating properly.

1. If television interference is occurring, note which channels are affected.

a. Lower harmonics of CB generally affect TV Channels 2, 5, 6, and 9. Therefore, if one or more of these channels are affected,

your transmitter is probably radiating harmonics.

b. If all TV channels are affected, the problem is more likely to be in the TV receiver.

2. If the interference is caused by harmonics, a spectrum analyzer, a calibrated field intensity meter, or frequency selective voltmeter, can be used to accurately measure harmonic and spurious radiations from your transmitter. If any lead-in devices, such as standing wave ratio (SWR) meters are used, measurements should be made with the in-line device both installed and removed. This may help identify the interference and lead you to the source. These are complex measurements and should normally be made only by experienced technicians.

3. If it appears that your transmitter is at fault, you should first make sure the chassis of the set is secured to the metal case of the radio by tightening the screws holding the chassis and case together. Then assure that the case of the transmitter is grounded to a good earth ground (metallic cold water pipe or 8 foot ground rod). Solid conductor wire of at least #10 gauge or copper ribbon should be used as a ground lead. The lead should be as short as possible.

4. By installing one or more low-pass filters in the transmitter antenna lead, you will reduce the chances of unnecessary harmonic radiation. A low-pass filter allows frequencies up to 30 or 50 megahertz (MHz), depending on brand, to pass through unattenuated to the antenna while effectively shorting out harmonic radiation. To make this test, connect the equipment as in Figure 21 and take a power reading. If only an SWR Bridge is available, calibrate it in the forward direction to the

calibrate line in the meter. Then insert the low-pass filter and make another power measurement. DO NOT retune the transmitter.

5. If you notice a decrease in output power on a power meter, operating to a properly matched load, with the low-pass filter installed, this is an indication that harmonic content may be present. Even though the meter reading may be lower with the filter installed, it does not mean that the transmitter absolutely has harmonic radiation. Slight de-tuning of the transmitter by the filter may cause a lower indication.

6. At amateur power levels, corroded metal connections in the area of the transmitting antenna may act like diodes and generate harmonics which may radiate. This type of problem can be found by vibrating suspected offenders such as galvanized downspouts, metal fences, clothes lines, etc., while view-

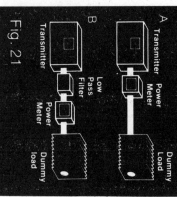

Fig. 21

A — Transmitter — Power Meter — Dummy Load

B — Transmitter — Low Pass Filter — Power Meter — Dummy load

ing the affected television set. Sudden changes in the interference pattern which correspond to the vibration should be noted. This test requires an observer at the TV receiver, someone to "shake" suspicious metal objects in the area, and another person to key (but NOT modulate) the transmitter involved.

7. Finally, some transmitters may actually be radiating harmonic and spurious energy from their cabinet or through the power lines. Try operating the transmitter into a shielded dummy load. If the interference is still present, then cabinet or power line radiation is indicated. A power line filter should be installed. Several types are commercially available. For low power transmitters, the filter in Figure 5 may be used.

8. Continued interference with the power line filter installed points toward cabinet radiation. An earth ground should eliminate cabinet radiation.

9. Local Television Interference (TVI) Committees dedicated to resolving CB-TVI problems are now being established. For assistance in locating a TVI Committee in your area, contact: International CB Radio Operators Association (CBA), P.O. Box 1020, Roanoke, Va., 24005.

Resolution of Interference for Amateur Transmitter Operators

1. If you have a linear amplifier on your amateur transmitting equipment, use two low-pass filters. One filter should be installed between the actual transmitter (exciter) and the input to the linear amplifier. (This prevents harmonics generated in the exciter from reaching the linear amplifier.) The second filter should be installed at the output of the linear amplifier to reduce harmonic and spurious content.

2. One unique interference problem to TV Channel 2 is from an amateur transmitter operating on the 6 meter band. This is due to the close proximity of the frequencies involved. You may wish to follow the procedures outlined in the Technical Information for Service Representatives section, page 11, to eliminate this type interference. You are not, however, required to service or add filtering to the complainant's television, and should not take any such action without the full co-operation of your neighbor.

3. Local Television Interference (TVI) Committees are available to assist you in resolving interference problems. Contact the nearest FCC district office (see addresses beginning on page 28) or the American Radio Relay League, Newington, Connecticut, for assistance in locating a TVI committee in your area.

Radio Transmitter Operator Guidelines for Resolving Audio Interference

Although audio interference (often called audio rectification) is usually resolved by modification of the affected device, you as a radio operator can take certain steps to reduce the possibility of audio rectification by eliminating circulating radio frequency (**RF**) currents in grounds and metal objects in the area.

1. Your radio transmitting equipment should be effectively grounded to a metallic cold water pipe or a ground rod driven into the ground at least 8 feet. The ground lead must be at least #10 wire or copper ribbon. The greater the surface area of the ground lead, the more effective it will be. Also, the ground lead should be as short as possible.

2. You are reminded that you are licensed to use only the amount of power necessary to establish communications. Operating with excessive power is likely to cause audio interference problems.

3. If you need assistance in performing the above modifications to your equipment, you can contact the dealer or manufacturer representatives. Also, an FCC-licensed service representative may be able to assist you.

It's awfully "cutsey" to use a special phonetic alphabet over the air but it impedes communication, so **forget it**. If your call is SM6TG, the temptation to use "send me 6 tall girls" will be difficult, but fight the urge! Below is the International Telecommunication Union Phonetic Alphabet. Clip this out and keep it near your rig until you have it memorized and use it automatically.

ICAO Phonetic Alphabet

A - Alpha
B - Bravo
C - Charlie
D - Delta
E - Echo
F - Foxtrot
G - Golf
H - Hotel
I - India
J - Juliet
K - Kilo
L - Lima
M - Mike

N - November
O - Oscar
P - Papa
Q - Quebec
R - Romeo
S - Sierra
T - Tango
U - Uniform
V - Victor
W - Wiskey
X - X-ray
Y - Yankee
Z - Zulu

ILLEGIMENTI NON CORBORUNDUM

Our operation has received indications that the opposition (they reside in Washington) may try to shut us down. Therefore, we're soliciting your help to keep us alive. A "warchest" has been suggested for legal fund. Sounds like a good idea. Should you care to make a donation, please make your check payable to:

THE FINAL EXAM Legal Defense Fund
c/o Bash Educational Services
P.O. Box 2115
San Leandro, California 94577

Unlike some other pleas/requests for funds for legal services, this one's no ripoff. All funds will be exclusively used for legal fees.

Should any of you readers be an attorney with background/interest in Federal cases (such as ours could become), you are invited to contribute your special expertise. I and/or our counsel (Mike—K2GMV) will be glad to brief you upon receipt of your letterhead request. There's a 1st Amendment question here plus Title 5 problems. Should you have an interesting offensive or defensive scenario, please let us hear from you.

I wish I could personally thank each of you for your warm regards and illustrations of support. A simple "thank you" is hardly enough.

HOURS OF OPERATION

You may telephone us at 415-352-5420 from 1700–0100 Zulu time during the months of April through October or from 1800–0200 Zulu during the months of November through March. If you haven't figured out Zulu time/GMT/UCT yet (why?), then please refer to the chart on the next page that describes the time conversions. Use Daylight Savings Times (E.D.S.T., C.D.S.T., etc.) from April through October and use the "regular" time columns for November through March.

During other times there will be a recording on the telephone where you may leave a message. Because of the expense involved we are unable to return long distance telephone calls.

TIME CONVERSION CHART

Below you will find a handy chart that allows you to convert local time to Coordinated Universal Time (U.T.C.). This used to be called Greenwich Mean Time or Zulu Time and is the international standard time usage based upon the Greenwich meridian or 0° longitude line. The National Bureau of Standards maintains radio stations WWV in Fort Collins, Colorado and WWVH in Hawaii. On the frequencies of 2.5, 5.0, 10.0, 15.0, and 20.0 megahertz, the National Bureau of Standards broadcasts standard time signals that have an accuracy far greater than ever required in amateur radio.

WWV and WWVH broadcast signals continuously during each day. Each second is marked by a signal or tick. The 59th second signal is omitted intentionally. A voice announcement of the time is given each minute at the 55 second point and is followed by the tick on the minute. The announcement sounds like this:

"At the tone, sixteen hours fifty-nine minutes Coordinated Universal Time"

A lot of information is broadcast over WWV and you can get the details on what they do by writing them at:

Radio Station WWV
Fort Collins, Colorado 80524

TIME CONVERSION CHART

BASH Educational Services Time	M.D.S.T.	C.D.S.T.	E.D.S.T.	U.T.C.	BASH Educational Services Time	M.S.T.	C.S.T.	E.S.T.
5 P.M.	6 P.M.	7 P.M.	8 P.M.	00:00	4 P.M.	5 P.M.	6 P.M.	7 P.M.
6 P.M.	7 P.M.	8 P.M.	9 P.M.	01:00	5 P.M.	6 P.M.	7 P.M.	8 P.M.
7 P.M.	8 P.M.	9 P.M.	10 P.M.	02:00	6 P.M.	7 P.M.	8 P.M.	9 P.M.
8 P.M.	9 P.M.	10 P.M.	11 P.M.	03:00	7 P.M.	8 P.M.	9 P.M.	10 P.M.
9 P.M.	10 P.M.	11 P.M.	Midnight	04:00	8 P.M.	9 P.M.	10 P.M.	11 P.M.
10 P.M.	11 P.M.	Midnight	1 A.M.	05:00	9 P.M.	10 P.M.	11 P.M.	Midnight
11 P.M.	Midnight	1 A.M.	2 A.M.	06:00	10 P.M.	11 P.M.	Midnight	1 A.M.
Midnight	1 A.M.	2 A.M.	3 A.M.	07:00	11 P.M.	Midnight	1 A.M.	2 A.M.
1 A.M.	2 A.M.	3 A.M.	4 A.M.	08:00	Midnight	1 A.M.	2 A.M.	3 A.M.
2 A.M.	3 A.M.	4 A.M.	5 A.M.	09:00	1 A.M.	2 A.M.	3 A.M.	4 A.M.
3 A.M.	4 A.M.	5 A.M.	6 A.M.	10:00	2 A.M.	3 A.M.	4 A.M.	5 A.M.
4 A.M.	5 A.M.	6 A.M.	7 A.M.	11:00	3 A.M.	4 A.M.	5 A.M.	6 A.M.
5 A.M.	6 A.M.	7 A.M.	8 A.M.	12:00	4 A.M.	5 A.M.	6 A.M.	7 A.M.
6 A.M.	7 A.M.	8 A.M.	9 A.M.	13:00	5 A.M.	6 A.M.	7 A.M.	8 A.M.
7 A.M.	8 A.M.	9 A.M.	10 A.M.	14:00	6 A.M.	7 A.M.	8 A.M.	9 A.M.
8 A.M.	9 A.M.	10 A.M.	11 A.M.	15:00	7 A.M.	8 A.M.	9 A.M.	10 A.M.
9 A.M.	10 A.M.	11 A.M.	Noon	16:00	8 A.M.	9 A.M.	10 A.M.	11 A.M.
10 A.M.	11 A.M.	Noon	1 P.M.	17:00	9 A.M.	10 A.M.	11 A.M.	Noon
11 A.M.	Noon	1 P.M.	2 P.M.	18:00	10 A.M.	11 A.M.	Noon	1 P.M.
Noon	1 P.M.	2 P.M.	3 P.M.	19:00	11 A.M.	Noon	1 P.M.	2 P.M.
1 P.M.	2 P.M.	3 P.M.	4 P.M.	20:00	Noon	1 P.M.	2 P.M.	3 P.M.
2 P.M.	3 P.M.	4 P.M.	5 P.M.	21:00	1 P.M.	2 P.M.	3 P.M.	4 P.M.
3 P.M.	4 P.M.	5 P.M.	6 P.M.	22:00	2 P.M.	3 P.M.	4 P.M.	5 P.M.
4 P.M.	5 P.M.	6 P.M.	7 P.M.	23:00	3 P.M.	4 P.M.	5 P.M.	6 P.M.

TO ERR IS HUMAN...

Should you find errors in the manual (except for some **deliberate** inaccuracies in the schematics), please write and let us know. We're not McGraw-Hill and my proofreading ability at 3 A.M. is pathetic. So, your comments are welcomed.

IS THERE A SPEAKER IN THE HOUSE?

If someone out there would be interested in cutting a master tape I would like to develop a cassette tape(s) that covers the material contained in this manual. It seems our unsighted friends, other handicapped individuals, and a portion of the balance of the ham population need this information on cassette.

Donate your time and facilities to cut a master tape and I'll dig up the quality cassette blanks needed for this project. Maybe together we can produce a couple hundred tapes and sell them at a small markup. Seems like we're neglecting a significant segment of our fellow hams otherwise.

Please get in touch if you would like to form a partnership in this endeavor. Ham Radio has geniuses in this field. Someone volunteer, please!

A NOTE TO CLASSROOM INSTRUCTORS

The Final Exam can be an asset to you for teaching theory. As you cover the syllabus you are using, please mention during the classroom instruction questions from this manual and then go on to explain the theory behind the question and answer. This way you are certain that you are covering the material that is being asked by the FCC.

What many instructors have done is to go through the manual and make up a reading list for their students. They tell the students to purchase The Final Exam along with their other study materials. You may say that this makes for a larger expenditure by the student but there is nothing cheap about ham radio, is there? No, of course not! Anyway, other instructors have typed up a reading list that goes along with their lectures.

For example, their list may say to review Questions 3, 14, 28, and 83 for Lesson #3. Again, you are covering the theory along with the practical aspects of passing the tests. I find far too many people who attended ham classes and spent their *time* and money (the time is usually more important) on the course and then failed the exam because the instructor didn't cover the material the FCC was asking about. It's great to have a background in theory but that doesn't count for much if you fail the FCC test. So, please help your students and help yourself by being certain that your lectures not only cover the theory you want your people to know but also cover the material the FCC is asking. That'll make your classes so successful you'll have a hard time refusing to do another class immediately!

As a note of interest, as an instructor you *should* have a copy of *Electronic Communication* by Robert L. Shrader. He presents radio theory in clear and easily readable words and also gets as complex as you'd care to go. I recommend that students *and* instructors buy the manual. The only drawback is the cost: $21.95. But there's another case of the fact that ham radio is *not* inexpensive! The ARRL manuals are o.k. but, with a few noteworthy exceptions, they do not cover the theory so that the *average* ham can understand what they're trying to say. This isn't meant to be a criticism of the ARRL. They do some things *very* well: QSL bureaus, Field Day, awards, and other contests. But their licensing manuals are not the best. They could be a whole lot better. I have people call me all the time complaining about this. How the devil can the average housewife or other non-technical person be expected to make any sense of that? They can't and it shows up when they take the FCC exams. So, help your people by recommending that they buy Shrader's book. It is available through bookstores, from Ham Radio Bookstore (they're the folks who publish HR Reports), or from us.

Together you and I can help the hams in their quest to upgrade. We *both* have an obligation to them because without them, where the hell would we be? For your additional info, I am working on a Novice theory book as well. Give me a call after February 1st to see what the status is and I promise you that it'll be a book a housewife can read and enjoy (no, I'm not a chauvinist pig; I *love* women and think we're not doing much to help them get on the air and intend to change that). Good luck and call me if I can help you in any way.

—MORE PROPAGANDA & NEAT INFO—

Your support of our dealers is appreciated. Should your favorite dealer not be listed here (this list is current as of December 1, 1980), please have him contact us.

Most dealers began stocking our test guide because hams went to them and suggested that they carry the books. So you **do** have an effect upon the dealer. We can offer your dealer an attractive program and at the same time make our manuals available to you locally. **PLEASE** (would you believe "pretty please"?) tell your dealer about our test guides and urge him to contact us at this address:

> Bash Educational Services
> P.O. Box 2115
> San Leandro, California 94577
> Telephone: 415-352-5420
> Attn: Dick Bash-KL7IHP

Thanks for all of **your** help and I wish you the very best when taking the test!

AGL Electronics, Inc.
Clearwater, Florida

Amateur & CB Radio Supply
New Brighton, Pennsylvania

Amateur Electronics Supply, Inc.
Las Vegas, Nevada

Amateur Electronics Supply, Inc.
Wickliffe, Ohio

Amateur Radio Center
Miami, Florida

Amateur Radio Supply
Seattle, Washington

A.R.S.O.N.
Nashville, Tennessee

Appliance & Equipment Co.
San Antonio, Texas

Aureus Electronics
Naperville, Illinois

The Base Station
Concord, California

Bob's Amateur Radio Center
Miami, Florida

Britt's Two-Way Radio
Smyrna, Georgia

Burghardt Amateur Center
Watertown, South Dakota

C.B. Sales & Service of Columbus
Columbus, Georgia

CLS Communications
Ravenswood, West Virginia

Carr Electronics
Telford, Pennsylvania

The Comm Center
Laurel, Maryland

Communications Center
Lincoln, Nebraska

Conley Radio Supply
Billings, Montana

C-Tronics
Ventura, California

CW Electronic Sales Co.
Denver, Colorado

D & L Discount Center
West Richland, Washington

Doc's Communications
Lookout Mountain, Tennessee

Dolphin Electronics
Seabrook, Texas

Donle Communications
Salem, Oregon

Don's Radio Communication
Wimbleton, North Dakota

Electronic Equipment Bank
Vienna, Virginia

Electronic Module
Hobbs, New Mexico

Eugene Radio Supply Inc.
Eugene, Oregon

Ferris Radio
Hazel Park, Michigan

Floyd Electronics
Collinsville, Illinois

Fontana Electronics
Fontana, California

Germantown Amateur Radio Supply, Inc.
Memphis, Tennessee

Gismo Communications
Rock Hill, South Carolina

Graham Electronics
Indianapolis, Indiana

Ham Radio Outlet
Anaheim, California

Ham Radio Outlet
Burlingame, California

Ham Radio Outlet
Oakland, California

Ham Radio Outlet
San Diego, California

Ham Radio Outlet
Van Nuys, California

Ham Radio World
Oriskany, New York

The Ham Shack
Lawrenceville, Georgia

The Ham Shack
Evansville, Indiana

Hamtronics
Trevose, Pennsylvania

Hanover Two-Way
Hanover, Indiana

Hardin Electronics
Fort Worth, Texas

Hatry Electronics
Hartford, Connecticut

Heathkit Electronics Center
Peabody, Massachusetts

Heathkit Electronic Center
Warwick, Rhode Island

HI., Inc.
Council Bluffs, Iowa

Hobbi-Tronics
San Jose, California

Honolulu Electronics
Honolulu, Hawaii

House of Electronics
Seaside, Oregon

Kryder Electronics
Ft. Wayne, Indiana

Kryder Electronics
Oklahoma City, Oklahoma

Kryder Electronics
Phoenix, Arizona

Long's Electronics
Birmingham, Alabama

Madison Electronics Supply
Houston, Texas

Mercer and Son
Shelton, Washington

Mid-Com Electronics Inc.
St. Louis, Missouri

Midway Electronics
Ferndale, Michigan

Missouri Communication Systems Inc.
Kansas City, Missouri

Norbill's Electronics Inc.
West Springfield, Massachusetts

Northwest Electronics
Bellevue, Ohio

Northwest Radio Supply, Inc.
Tacoma, Washington

Pal Electronics Inc.
Minneapolis, Minnesota

Pioneer—Standard Electronics
Dayton, Ohio

Quad Electronics
Pensacola, Florida

Quement Electronics
San Jose, California

Radio Inc.
Tulsa, Oklahoma

The Radio Place
Sacramento, California

Radio Service Center
Denver, Colorado

Ray's Amateur Radio
Clearwater, Florida

Rick's Radio Repair
Chicago, Illinois

Ross Distributing
Preston, Idaho

RSE Ham Shack
Clawson, Michigan

Rush Electronics
Bristol, Tennessee

Selectronics
Sacramento, California

Sere-Rose Electronics, Inc.
Memphis, Tennessee

Shawnee Electronics
New Boston, Ohio

Spectronics, Inc.
Oak Park, Illinois

Sword Enterprises
Adrian, Michigan

Tel—Com
Littleton, Massachusetts

Tufts Radio & Electronics
Medford, Massachusetts

Universal Amateur Radio, Inc.
Columbus, Ohio

Webster Radio, Inc.
Fresno, California

Wittie Electronics
Clifton, New Jersey

THE INFAMOUS 007½ CERTIFICATE
(and how you can get one)

Recognizing the strength that is sapped from you during the exams, we have felt it necessary to award the 007½ certificate to those who sent in their completed Feedback Sheets (or, if you don't want to tear your page out, then send the information to us on darn near anything but toilet paper). So, when we receive your Feedback Sheet, we will send you (at no charge whatsoever) a beautiful certificate suitable for framing. This certificate is given in recognition of the major intelligence coup you have accomplished. Some of the guys asked for a weekend on a desert isle with a #10 and the gals raved for Burt Reynolds but we defied those vain and sinful requests and came up with this neat wallpaper instead. Get yours by filling out the doggone Feedback Sheet and sending it off as soon as you take the exam.

Send this to your favorite dealer or to us for additional copies.

THE FINAL EXAM
ORDER FORM
(Don't copy this book, darn it! Order it! We need the $$$)

Name _____

Address_____

City_____ State_____ Zip_____

Callsign_____

☐ **General Class** ($9.95 each) $ _____

☐ **Advanced Class** ($9.95 each) $ _____

☐ **Extra Class** ($9.95 each) $ _____

**Postage and handling
($1.50 1st Class Mailing —
$2.25 for U.P.S each book)** $ _____

Total Enclosed $ _____

If you send this order to us, we'll ship within **48** hours of receipt by 1st Class Mail or U.P.S.

**Bash Educational Services
P.O. Box 2115
San Leandro, California 94577
415-352-5420**

ARRL PUBLICATIONS

As a service to those readers who do not have access to an amateur radio store to purchase the American Radio Relay League's publications, we have been granted a dealership by the ARRL to stock their books. We list below selected publications and the prices for them. So, if you're out in the sticks, unable to get downtown to the local ham store, or whatever, then you may wish to order the ARRL books from us. Your total cost will also include the charge of 15% for shipping, so be sure to add that in to your order. These books will be shipped via llama or the like and will take about 14 days to get to you. If you'll double the shipping charges, we will ship via 1st class mail.

Qty	Title	Cost	Shipping	Total Charges
	Radio Amateur's Handbook (1981)	$10.00	$1.50	$11.50
	Antenna Book	5.00	.75	5.75
	The Basic Book of Ham Radio	4.95	.75	5.70
	Solid State Basics	5.00	.75	5.75
	Radio Frequency Interference	3.00	.45	3.45
	U.S. Call Area Map	3.00	.45	3.45
	Tune in the World with Ham Radio	7.00	1.05	8.05
	ARRL Code Tape Kit	8.00	1.20	9.20
	Log Book (regular size)	1.75	.30	2.05
	Mini Log Book	.75	.15	.90
	Pad of 50 ARRL Traffic Message Blanks	.75	.15	.90
	ARRL VHF Repeater Directory	1.00	.15	1.15
	QST Binder for magazine	7.00	1.05	8.05

The lads and lasses living in the great state of California will have to add 6½% sales tax also. Because this is just a breakeven type of service, **we will have to insist on a minimum order of $10.00.**

We wish to thank the ARRL for allowing us this opportunity to serve the ham community. We will be happy to ship these products to you COD if you wish (UPS only—no P.O. boxes).

And God said . . .

$$\frac{mv^2}{r} = \frac{Ze^2}{r^2}$$

$$mvr = \frac{nh}{2\pi}$$

$$r = \frac{r^2h^2}{(2\pi)^2mZe^2}$$

$$E = \frac{1}{2}mv^2 - Z\frac{e^2}{r}$$

$$E = \frac{2\pi mZ^2e^4}{n^2h^2} = Ry$$

. . . and there was Light.

— CORRECTIONS TO THE ADVANCED CLASS MANUAL —

1. On **Page 6, Question 21**, we left the values out of the schematic. The capacitor is 25 ohms, the resistor is 100 ohms, and the coil is 50 ohms. Please mark these values on the schematic.

2. On **Page 11, Question 31**, in about the middle of the page, we left the horizontal line out of the fraction. Please put a horizontal line between the words *input voltage (primary)* and the line below it that says *output voltage (secondary)*. Also put a horizontal line between the line that says *turns (primary)* and the one below it that says *turns (secondary)*.

3. On **Page 40, Question 135**, the schematic on the left is *schematic A* and the schematic on the right is *schematic B*.

   Please note that we are *not* saying that these resistors are in parallel but merely that you must treat them *mathematically* as if they were in parallel. If you're not familar with Thevinen's theorem, then you'll just have trust us on this one. This *is* the way to solve this problem and get the 2 points on the exam!.

FEEDBACK

Name_____ Callsign_____

Address _____

City_____ State_____ Zip_____

I took my General/Advanced/Extra Class exam (circle where applicable) at the F.C.C.

office in _____ on _____ My examination number

(shown somewhere on the cover page of the test) was _____ Each
question had a choice of four/five (cross out where applicable) answers.
I ☐ Passed   ☐ Failed

I recall the following question(s) were on my test:

1. _____

_____

_____

2. _____

_____

_____

3. _____

_____

FEEDBACK

Name_____ Callsign_____

Address _____

City_____ State_____ Zip_____

I took my General/Advanced/Extra Class exam (circle where applicable) at the F.C.C.

office in _____ on _____ My examination number

(shown somewhere on the cover page of the test) was _____ Each
question had a choice of four/five (cross out where applicable) answers.
I ☐ Passed   ☐ Failed

I recall the following question(s) were on my test:

1. _____

_____

_____

2. _____

_____

_____

3. _____

_____

BASH EDUCATIONAL SERVICES
P.O. BOX 2115
SAN LEANDRO, CALIFORNIA 94577

BASH EDUCATIONAL SERVICES
P.O. BOX 2115
SAN LEANDRO, CALIFORNIA 94577